AS Biology
UNITS 2&3

Edexcel

Unit 2: Exchange, Transport and Reproduction

Unit 3: Energy and the Environment

Alan Clamp

To Aristos, Dave, Jon, Jules, Paul and Pete.

Philip Allan Updates
Market Place
Deddington
Oxfordshire
OX15 0SE

tel: 01869 338652
fax: 01869 337590
e-mail: sales@philipallan.co.uk
www.philipallan.co.uk

© Philip Allan Updates 2001
Revised September 2002

ISBN 0 86003 470 4

This Guide has been written specifically to support students preparing for the Edexcel AS Biology Unit 2 and Unit 3 examinations. The content has been neither approved nor endorsed by Edexcel and remains the sole responsibility of the author.

Typeset by Magnet Harlequin, Oxford
Printed by Information Press, Eynsham, Oxford

Contents

Introduction

■ ■ ■

Content Guidance

■ ■ ■

Questions and answers

Introduction

About this guide

This unit guide is the second book in a series of four, which together cover the whole Edexcel specification for AS and A-level biology. Its aim is to help you prepare for Unit Tests 2 and 3 in AS Biology which examine the content of **Unit 2: Exchange, Transport and Reproduction** and **Unit 3: Energy and the Environment**. There are three sections to this guide:

- **Introduction** — this provides advice on how to use the unit guide, an explanation of the skills required in AS biology and suggestions for effective revision. It concludes with guidance on how to succeed in the unit tests.
- **Content Guidance** — this summarises the specification content of Units 2 and 3.
- **Questions and Answers** — this provides two Unit 2 mock test papers and two Unit 3 mock test papers for you to try, together with sample answers to these questions and examiner's comments on how these answers could have been improved.

An effective way to use this book is to read through this Introduction section to familiarise yourself with the skills required in AS biology. Try to make a habit of using the study skills and revision advice suggested in this section. It may also help to refer back to this information at regular intervals during your course. The Content Guidance will be useful when you are revising a topic because it highlights the main points of each subsection of Units 2 and 3 of the specification. You may want to 'tick-off' topics as you learn them to make sure that you have revised everything thoroughly. Finally, the mock tests in the Question and Answer section will provide some very useful practice when preparing for the unit tests.

The specification

In order to make a good start to Units 2 and 3, it is important to have a close look at the specification (syllabus). Your teacher should have one, or you can obtain your own copy from the awarding body (Edexcel). In addition to describing the content of the units, the specification provides information about the unit tests. It is important for you to understand the key terms used in the specification, as defined below.

- **Recall** — identify and revise biological knowledge gained from previous studies of biology.
- **Know** — be able to state facts, or describe structures and processes, from material within the unit.
- **Understand** — explain the underlying principles and apply this knowledge to new situations.

- **Appreciate** — be aware of the importance of biological information, without having a detailed knowledge of the underlying principles.
- **Discuss** — give a balanced, reasoned and objective review of a particular topic.
- **Describe** — provide an accurate account of the main points (an explanation is not necessary).
- **Explain** — give reasons, with reference to biological theories.

The specification also provides information about the skills required in AS biology. For example, in Unit 2 approximately two-thirds of the marks are available for showing *knowledge and understanding* of biological information, and one-third of the marks are available for *applying* this knowledge and understanding to explain experimental data or solve problems in unfamiliar situations. In the written paper for Unit 3, however, there is a greater emphasis on the application of knowledge and understanding. In addition, approximately half the total marks available for Unit 3 are for the practical assessment of coursework, as described on page 9.

Finally, in addition to looking at the specification, it would be useful for you to read the examiners' reports and published mark schemes from previous unit tests (these are available from Edexcel). These documents will show you the depth of knowledge that examiners are looking for in answers, as well as pointing out common mistakes and providing advice on how to achieve good grades in the tests.

Study skills and revision strategies

Students need to develop good study skills if they are to be successful. This section of the Introduction provides advice and guidance on how to study AS biology, as well as some strategies for effective revision.

Organising your notes

Biology students usually accumulate a large quantity of notes and it is useful to keep this information in an organised manner. The presentation of notes is important; good notes should always be clear and concise. You could try organising your notes under headings and subheadings, with key points highlighted using capitals, italics or colour. Numbered lists are useful, as are tables and diagrams. It is a good idea to file your notes in specification order, using a consistent series of informative headings, as illustrated below.

> ### UNIT 2 (Exchange, Transport and Reproduction)
> **Transport in mammals: the structure and roles of arteries, veins and capillaries**
> *Arteries*
> *Arteries are vessels that carry blood away from the heart...*

After the lessons, it is a good idea to check your notes using your textbook(s) and fill in any gaps in the information. Make sure you go back and ask the teacher if you are unsure about anything, especially if you find conflicting information in your class notes and textbook.

Organising your time

When trying to organise your time, it is a good idea to make a revision timetable. This should allow enough time to cover all the material, but also be realistic. For example, it is useful to leave some time at the end of the timetable, just before the unit tests, to catch up on time lost, for example through illness. You may not be able to work for very long at a single session — probably no more than 1 hour without a short break of 10–15 minutes. It is also useful to use spare moments, such as when waiting for a bus or train, to do short snippets of revision. These 'odd minutes' can add up to many hours.

Improving your memory

There are several things you can do to improve the effectiveness of your memory for biological information. Organising the material will help, especially if you use topic headings, numbered lists and diagrams. Repeatedly reviewing your notes will also be useful, as will discussing topics with teachers and other students. Finally, using mnemonics (memory aids), such as **A**rteries carry blood **A**way from the heart, can make a big difference.

Revision strategies

To revise a topic effectively, you should work carefully through your notes, using a copy of the specification to make sure you have not missed anything out. Summarise your notes to the bare essentials, using the tips given on note-making above. Finally, use the content guidance and mock examinations in this book, discussing any difficulties with your teachers or other students.

In many ways, a student should prepare for a unit test like an athlete prepares for a major event, such as the Olympic Games. The athlete will train every day for weeks or months before the event, practising the required skills in order to achieve the best performance on the day. So it is with test preparation: everything you do should contribute to your chances of success in the unit test. The following points summarise some of the strategies that you may wish to use to make sure that your revision is as effective as possible.

- Use a revision timetable.
- Ideally, revise in a quiet room, sitting at a desk or table, with no distractions.
- Test yourself regularly to assess the effectiveness of revision.
- Practise previous test questions to highlight gaps in your knowledge and understanding, and to improve your technique.

- Active revision is much better than simply reading over material. Discuss topics, summarise notes and use the mock tests included in this book to increase the effectiveness of your revision.

The unit tests

Unit Test 2 consists of about nine compulsory questions allocated from 4 to 12 marks each, presented in a question–answer booklet. There are 70 marks available in the test and it lasts for 1 hour and 15 minutes (giving you approximately 1 minute per mark). The shorter questions are designed mainly to test knowledge and understanding of the unit content. The longer questions also test skills of interpretation of data that are related to the content of the unit. There is normally one free-prose question on each paper (see p. 8).

The written test in Unit 3 typically consists of three compulsory questions allocated from 6 to 20 marks each, presented in a question–answer booklet. There are 38 marks available in the test and it lasts for 1 hour (giving you approximately $1\frac{1}{2}$ minutes per mark). The shorter questions are designed to test mainly knowledge and understanding of the content of the unit. The longer questions contain stimulus material related to the unit and test both knowledge and data interpretation skills. Unit 3 also includes practical assessment of coursework, as described on page 9.

There are a number of terms commonly used in unit tests. It is important that you understand the meaning of each of these terms and that you answer the question appropriately.

- **Calculate** — carry out a calculation, showing your working and providing the appropriate units.
- **Compare** — point out similarities *and* differences.
- **Define** — give a statement outlining what is meant by a particular term.
- **Describe** — provide an accurate account of the main points. An explanation is *not* necessary.
- **Discuss** — describe and evaluate, putting forward the various opinions on a topic.
- **Distinguish between** — point out differences only.
- **Explain** — give reasons, with reference to biological facts. A description is *not* required.
- **Outline** — give a brief account.
- **Significance** — the relevance of an idea or observation.
- **State** — give a concise, factual answer (also applies to **give** or **name**).
- **Suggest** — use biological knowledge to put forward an appropriate answer in an unfamiliar situation.
- **What/Why/Where** — these indicate direct questions requiring concise answers.

Whatever the question style, you must read the question *very carefully*, underline key words or phrases, think about your response and allocate time according to the number of marks available. Further advice and guidance on answering test questions is provided in the Question and Answer section at the end of this book.

Structured questions

These are short-answer questions that may require a single word answer, a short sentence, or a response amounting to several sentences. Answers should be clear, concise and to the point. The marks allocated and the space provided for the answer usually give an indication of the amount of detail required. Typical question styles include:
- naming parts on diagrams
- filling in gaps in a prose passage
- completing tables and tick-boxes
- plotting graphs
- performing calculations
- interpreting experimental data

Free-prose questions

These questions enable you to demonstrate the depth and breadth of your biological knowledge, as well as your ability to communicate scientific ideas in a concise and clear manner. The following points should help you to perform well when answering free-prose questions:
- make your points clearly and concisely, illustrating with examples where appropriate
- try to avoid repetition and keep the answer relevant (refer back to the question)
- the points made should cover the *full range* of the topic addressed in the question
- use diagrams only if appropriate and where they make a useful contribution to the quality of your answer
- spend the appropriate amount of time on the question (proportional to the marks available)

The day of the unit test

On the day of the test, make sure that you have:
- two or more blue/black pens, and two or more pencils
- your calculator plus spare batteries
- a watch to check the time
- a ruler and an eraser

Read each question very carefully so that your answers are appropriate. Make sure that you write legibly (you will not be given marks if the examiner cannot read what you have written) and try to spell scientific terms accurately. If you need more room for your answer, look for space at the bottom of the page, the end of the question or after the last question, or use supplementary sheets. If you use these spaces, or sheets, alert the examiner by adding 'continued below', or 'continued on page X'.

Time is often a problem. Make sure that you know how long you have got for the whole test and how many questions you have to do in this time. You could use the number of minutes per mark to work out approximately how long you have for each question (e.g. 7 minutes for a 7-mark question in Unit Test 2).

Do not write out the question, but try to make a number of valid points that correspond to the number of marks available. If you get stuck, make a note of the question number and move on. Later, if you have time, go back and try that difficult question again. Finally, it is a good idea to leave a few minutes at the end to check through the paper, correcting any mistakes or filling in any gaps.

Practical assessment of coursework

The individual investigation in Unit 3 involves the assessment of practical skills through coursework. The aim of the investigation is to give you the opportunity to plan and carry out a scientific experiment on your own. You then need to write a detailed account of your investigation, which is marked by your teacher and then moderated (i.e. the marking is checked) by Edexcel.

In the individual investigation, marks are awarded for:
- planning
- implementing
- analysing evidence and drawing conclusions
- evaluating evidence and procedures

It is very useful to have a copy of the marking scheme when you are planning, carrying out and writing up your investigation. You are more likely to get a good grade if you know how the marks are awarded. Further information about the practical assessment of coursework can be found in the specification.

Content
Guidance

Unit 2: Exchange, Transport and Reproduction

Unit 2 is divided into five topics:

(1) Exchanges with the environment

(2) Digestion and absorption

(3) Transport systems

(4) Adaptations to the environment

(5) Sexual reproduction

Unit 3: Energy and the Environment

Unit 3 is divided into five topics:

(1) Modes of nutrition

(2) Ecosystems

(3) Energy flow

(4) Recycling of nutrients

(5) Human influences on the environment

You may be familiar with some of the information in these units, but it is important that you know and understand this information exactly as described in the specification. This summary of the specification content will highlight the key points and should prove very useful when learning and revising biology.

Exchanges with the environment

Exchange processes

All living organisms need to exchange materials with their environment, taking in oxygen and nutrients, and releasing carbon dioxide and other excretory products.

Single-celled organisms rely upon simple **diffusion**, but multicellular organisms require specialised exchange surfaces. For example, a small one-celled organism, such as a protozoan, has a very large surface area-to-volume (SA/V) ratio. It is therefore able to gain all the oxygen it requires by diffusion through its body surface. A larger organism, such as a human, however, has a much smaller SA/V ratio and needs a specially adapted gas-exchange surface (the lungs) in order to obtain sufficient oxygen. Similarly, larger organisms also need a specially adapted surface for the digestion and absorption of nutrients (see pages 15–16).

Exchange surfaces are usually adapted to ensure that substances can move in and out efficiently. Typical features include:
- a large surface area-to-volume ratio
- a small diffusion distance
- membrane-bound carriers to aid **facilitated diffusion** and **active transport**
- a mechanism for maintaining the concentration gradient, such as a **counter-current system** (in which fluids in adjacent systems flow in opposite directions in order to maintain a diffusion gradient between them) or a **ventilation system**, such as the lungs

Gas exchange in flowering plants

The key structures within the leaf that allow the exchange of oxygen and carbon dioxide are **stomata**, which are pores found in the epidermis of a plant. Stomata are present in very large numbers, especially on the underside of leaves. They are concerned with gas exchange for **respiration** and **photosynthesis**, and also with the loss of water vapour by **transpiration**.

Stomata can be opened or closed by guard cells according to the requirements of the plant, often being open in the day (to provide carbon dioxide for photosynthesis) and closed at night (to minimise water loss). It is important for you to learn the precise mechanisms involved in the opening and closing of stomata.

In order to understand how gas exchange is achieved in flowering plants, you need to know the structure of a leaf, as shown in the following diagram.

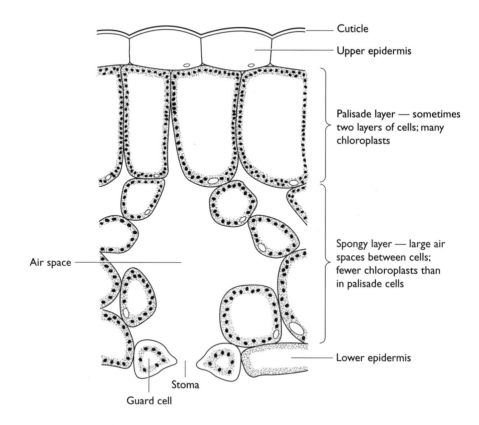

- Cuticle
- Upper epidermis
- Palisade layer — sometimes two layers of cells; many chloroplasts
- Spongy layer — large air spaces between cells; fewer chloroplasts than in palisade cells
- Air space
- Lower epidermis
- Stoma
- Guard cell

Gas exchange in humans

The mechanism by which respiratory gases are delivered to and from a gas-exchange surface is known as **ventilation**. For gas exchange to occur efficiently, the air in contact with the exchange surface must be changed regularly. This maintains a diffusion gradient for the respiratory gases. Humans use muscles in the diaphragm and between the ribs to pump air in and out of the **lungs**. The lungs are composed of air ducts (the trachea, bronchi and bronchioles) and alveoli, which provide a very large surface area for gas exchange with the blood. The mechanisms of inspiration (breathing in) and expiration (breathing out) are summarised in the table below.

	Inspiration	**Expiration**
Diaphragm	Contracts	Relaxes
External intercostal muscles	Contract	Relax
Internal intercostal muscles	Relax	Contract
Volume of thorax	Increases	Decreases
Pressure in lungs	Decreases	Increases
Air movement	In	Out

The rate of ventilation is carefully controlled to ensure that body cells have an adequate supply of oxygen for aerobic respiration. The diagram below summarises the processes involved in regulating the ventilation rate.

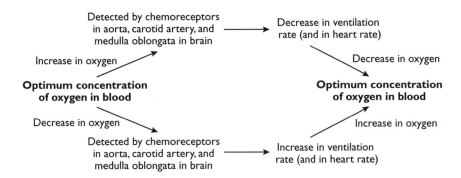

Finally, you will be expected to have carried out practical work on the use of simple respirometers in relation to gas exchange.

Digestion and absorption

Digestion

This is the breaking down of food material into simple molecules that can be absorbed by the body. It involves both physical and chemical processes. **Physical digestion** is the action of teeth and gut muscles, which helps to break up food and mix it with digestive juices. In **chemical digestion**, bile breaks down fat into tiny droplets while hydrolytic enzymes complete the process of digestion by breaking down the individual food molecules. For example, lipase, a digestive enzyme produced by the pancreas, hydrolyses lipids into fatty acids and glycerol.

There are a number of enzymes involved in the digestion of carbohydrates and you should know where each one is produced, its substrates and products, and the conditions under which it works best. This information is summarised in the table below.

Site of action	Optimum pH	Enzyme(s)	Substrate	Product(s)
Mouth	7.0	Salivary amylase	Starch	Maltose
Duodenum	7.0	Pancreatic amylase	Starch	Maltose
Ileum	8.5	Maltase	Maltose	Glucose
		Lactase	Lactose	Glucose and galactose
		Sucrase	Sucrose	Glucose and fructose

It is also important to know the structure of the digestive system (**alimentary canal**) and the mechanism by which food moves along the gut (**peristalsis**).

Absorption

This is the process by which dissolved substances are taken up by cells. It occurs across the cells lining the **ileum**. The ileum is designed for efficient absorption.

- It is long, with large numbers of finger-like projections called villi, providing a large surface area.
- The individual lining cells possess microvilli, which further increase the surface area. Many cells also contain large numbers of mitochondria, which provide the ATP necessary for active transport and endocytosis.
- Contraction and relaxation of smooth muscle in the ileum wall mixes the digested food and maintains a diffusion gradient.
- Each villus has an extensive capillary system and a lacteal to transport away the absorbed products.

Transport systems

Large multicellular organisms need transport systems for the same reasons as they need specialised exchange surfaces (see p. 13). An important concept to understand when learning about transport systems is **mass transport**. This is the transport of molecules in bulk from one part of an organism to another, via the **blood system** in animals or the **phloem** and **xylem** in plants.

Transport in flowering plants

In order to understand how substances are transported in flowering plants, you first need to know the structure of the vascular tissues.

Xylem is the vascular tissue concerned with the transport of water and inorganic salts. Xylem tissue is composed of **tracheids** and **vessels**. Tracheids are elongated cells that contain large quantities of lignin in their cell walls; their end-walls are perforated by a number of pores which allow water to move through the plant from one tracheid to the next. Vessels are also elongated cells containing large quantities of lignin in their cell walls; their end-walls are broken down during development to provide connections with other vessel cells above and below (rather like a drainpipe), allowing efficient movement of water through the plant. Xylem also contains fibres and xylem parenchyma. Water generally moves up the xylem from the roots to the stem and leaves, as described by the **cohesion–tension theory** (see below).

Phloem is the vascular tissue concerned with the transport of soluble organic molecules, such as sucrose and amino acids. Phloem tissue is composed of **sieve tube**

elements (living cells separated by perforated sieve plates, forming long conducting tubes) and **companion cells** (living cells which are connected to sieve tube elements by plasmodesmata and assist in the transport of organic materials). Phloem also contains fibres and phloem parenchyma. It transports organic molecules from the site of production in the leaves (the **source**) to the other parts of the plant (the **sink**). It is thought that the molecules move by a system of mass flow.

Movement of water

Water is taken up into plants via the **roots** (you are expected to know the structure of a root). It then moves through the plant by one of three pathways.

- In the **apoplastic pathway** water moves through the **cell walls** of plant cells.
- In the **symplastic pathway** water moves through the **cytoplasm** and **plasmodesmata** of plant cells.
- In the **vacuolar pathway** water moves through the **vacuoles** of plant cells.

The endodermal cells in plant roots contain a **Casparian strip**, which is a band of impermeable suberin. This prevents water and solutes from entering the xylem via the apoplastic pathway. As a result, these substances have to pass along the symplastic pathway. This allows the plant to control the movement of water and solutes into the xylem.

Water moves through the plant according to the **cohesion–tension theory**, which is summarised in the diagram below.

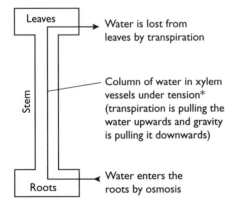

* The water molecules are held together by **cohesion** (forces of attraction between the molecules) and the column is under **tension**. Water molecules are also attracted to the walls of the xylem vessels (adhesion) and this helps to pull the water upwards.

Transpiration occurs mainly through the **stomata** on leaves, but also to a lesser extent through the lenticels on woody stems. This loss of water vapour creates a **water potential gradient** which draws water up the xylem according to the cohesion–tension theory.

The rate of transpiration is increased by increasing the temperature, light intensity or wind speed, or decreasing the relative humidity around the plant.

Finally, you will be expected to have carried out the following practical work in relation to your work on the movement of water:

- demonstrations and measurements of transpiration using a potometer
- stomatal counts

Movement of nutrients

Mineral ions are taken up by root cells by diffusion and active transport, and moved through the plant as solutes in water. However, organic solutes do *not* travel through the xylem, but are **translocated** via the phloem. Organic molecules, such as **sucrose** and **amino acids**, are transported from a site of production (e.g. the photosynthetic cells in a leaf) to other parts of the plant via the phloem tissue. In other words, they move from a **source** to a **sink**. Although most biologists believe that substances move through the phloem by a system of mass flow, the precise mechanisms are unknown.

Transport in mammals

The circulatory system in mammals transports **blood** (containing respiratory gases, metabolites, metabolic wastes and hormones) around the body. All blood circulatory systems have a pump (the **heart**) and a series of blood vessels (**arteries**, **veins** and **capillaries**). Mammals have a **double circulation** — blood passes through the heart twice as it travels around the body. Blood is pumped from the right side of the heart to the lungs in order to receive oxygen. It then returns to the left side of the heart before being pumped around the rest of the body. This is much more efficient than the **single circulation** system seen in fish, because the tissues are always supplied with oxygen-rich blood at high pressure.

The generalised structure of a mammalian heart is shown in the diagram below.

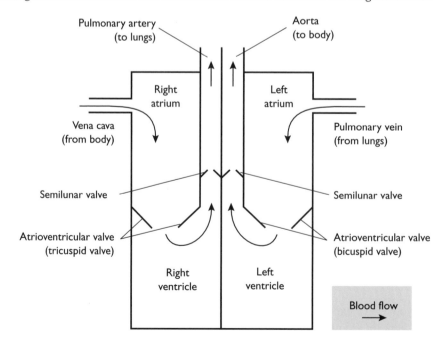

(Note that it is easy to confuse the left and right sides of the heart, the names of the associated blood vessels and the direction of blood flow. It is important that you know and understand this information.)

The pumping action of the heart is described by the **cardiac cycle**, which is the sequence of events taking place in a single heartbeat. The heartbeat is initiated by a small area of muscle tissue in the wall of the right **atrium** known as the **sino-atrial (SA) node** or pacemaker. This causes the following events:

(1) **Atrial systole** — the atria contract, forcing blood into the **ventricles**.
(2) **Ventricular systole** — the ventricles contract, forcing blood out of the heart.
(3) **Atrial and ventricular diastole** — the atria and ventricles relax and the heart refills.

Atrial and ventricular diastole are then followed by atrial systole, and the cycle continues. The speed of the cycle (controlled by the SA node) can be influenced by two nerves from the brain: the cardiac accelerator nerve (part of the **sympathetic nervous system**) increases the rate at which the heart beats; and the vagus nerve (part of the **parasympathetic nervous system**) decreases the rate at which the heart beats.

The three main types of blood vessel are **arteries**, **veins** and **capillaries**.

Arteries are vessels that carry blood away from the heart. All arteries carry oxygenated blood, except the **pulmonary artery**, which transports blood from the heart to the lungs. Arterial blood is under high pressure, so the walls of the arteries contain elastic tissue that helps to even out the pulsed flow. The walls of smaller arteries are particularly rich in **smooth muscle** fibres. This muscle enables the arteries to alter their diameter and so helps to regulate the blood supply to a particular organ, although this happens mainly in **arterioles**.

Veins are vessels that carry blood towards the heart. All veins carry deoxygenated blood, except the **pulmonary vein**, which transports blood from the lungs to the heart. Venous blood is at low pressure, so the walls of the veins contain much less muscle and elastic tissue than those of arteries. Contractions of the skeletal muscles around the veins squeeze blood along the vessels and **semilunar valves** help to prevent backflow. As a result, the flow of blood back to the heart is maintained.

Capillaries are very small blood vessels where water, solutes and respiratory gases are exchanged with body tissues. Capillaries carry blood from arterioles to venules. Their walls are only one cell thick, so oxygen and nutrients can pass easily into the surrounding tissues. Similarly, waste materials, such as urea and carbon dioxide, can enter capillaries from the tissues and be transported away for excretion.

Blood and body fluids

Blood is a suspension of cells in solution which acts as a transport medium within an animal. In humans, blood consists of about 55% by volume of **plasma** and 45% by volume of cells. The cells consist of **red blood cells** (erythrocytes), **white blood cells** (leucocytes) and small cell fragments called platelets. Blood has a number of important biological functions, including protection against disease and transport.

- **Protection against disease** — white blood cells produce antibodies and remove microorganisms by phagocytosis; platelets are important in blood clotting to prevent the entry of microorganisms.
- **Transport** — of nutrients, such as glucose and amino acids; respiratory gases (oxygen and carbon dioxide); excretory products, such as urea; hormones, such as insulin; and heat.

Red blood cells are specialised for transporting respiratory gases in the blood. Each cell is about 8 μm in diameter and has a biconcave shape, providing a high surface area-to-volume ratio, for efficient gas exchange. Mammalian red blood cells have no nucleus, enabling them to carry large amounts of **haemoglobin**. Haemoglobin is an iron-containing protein which consists of four polypeptide chains, each linked to a haem group. Its function is to transport oxygen around the body, each haem group combining reversibly with an oxygen molecule. This can be summarised as follows:

$$Hb \quad + \quad 4O_2 \quad \underset{\text{respiring tissues}}{\overset{\text{lungs}}{\rightleftharpoons}} \quad Hb(O_2)_4$$

haemoglobin oxygen oxyhaemoglobin

The relationship between the concentration of oxygen in the blood and the percentage saturation of haemoglobin is shown by the **oxygen dissociation curve**. The diagram below shows a typical oxygen dissociation curve for human haemoglobin.

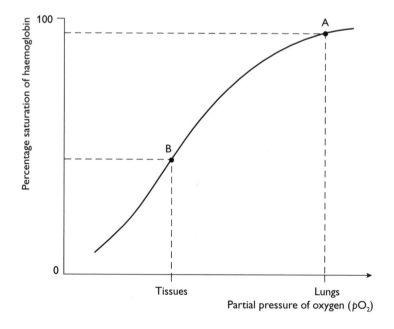

The steep rise of the curve at low partial pressures of oxygen indicates that a small change in pO_2 (partial pressure of oxygen) results in a relatively large change in the saturation of haemoglobin with oxygen. Therefore, in the lungs, where the pO_2 is high (A), the blood is rapidly saturated with oxygen. Similarly, in rapidly respiring tissues, where the pO_2 is low (B), oxygen is released from haemoglobin for use by the tissues. The affinity of haemoglobin for oxygen depends upon the concentration of carbon dioxide in the blood, as described by the **Bohr effect**.

(Note that if the curve moves to the *left*, haemoglobin has a *higher* affinity for oxygen. Likewise, if it moves to the *right*, haemoglobin has a *lower* affinity for oxygen. Try to remember that a shift to the **R**ight makes it more likely that haemoglobin will **R**elease oxygen.)

In addition to its oxygen-carrying function, haemoglobin transports some carbon dioxide (as carbamino compounds, *not* carboxyhaemoglobin) and is also an important **buffer** in the blood.

There are several different types of white blood cell (leucocyte), but they all contain a nucleus and are involved in coordinating the immune response. For example, lymphocytes produce antibodies, and neutrophils and monocytes ingest bacteria by phagocytosis.

The liquid part of the blood is called **plasma**. It is about 95% water and contains a number of dissolved substances:
- **proteins** — e.g. fibrinogen for blood clotting
- **inorganic ions** — e.g. Na^+, K^+, Cl^- and HCO_3^-
- **nutrients** — e.g. glucose and amino acids
- **hormones** — e.g. insulin
- **vitamins** — e.g. vitamin C
- **excretory materials** — e.g. urea and carbon dioxide

Tissue fluid (the fluid that surrounds the cells in an animal) is formed when blood plasma is forced out of capillaries by ultrafiltration. High pressure at the arterial end of the capillaries forces the plasma out of the capillaries and into the intercellular spaces. Tissue fluid has the same composition as plasma, except that it lacks plasma proteins which are too large to leave the capillaries. It is the medium from which cells take up nutrients and respiratory gases, and into which they release waste products. At the venous end of the capillaries (where pressure is low), the tissue fluid is taken back into the blood by **osmosis**. Any excess fluid around the cells is taken up by **lymph** vessels.

Finally, you will be expected to have carried out practical work on the microscopic examination of stained blood films and on the identification of cells.

UNIT

Adaptations to the environment

All species are adapted to survive in particular environmental conditions. An adaptation is any feature of the structure, physiology or behaviour of an organism that makes it well suited to its environment.

Organisms that are better adapted to their environment are more likely to survive and reproduce than those that are less well adapted. If these adaptations are genetically controlled, the next generation will have a higher proportion of well-adapted individuals (assuming that there are no major environmental changes). Eventually, these adaptations will be shown by the vast majority of the species. **Natural selection** of inheritable adaptations can ultimately lead to the development of new species.

Structural adaptation

In general, the external features of organisms are adapted to the physical characteristics of a particular habitat. For example, many invertebrates show structural adaptations to the varying oxygen concentrations found in fresh water. These include external gills, structures providing direct access to air, and the presence of respiratory pigments.

A good example of structural adaptation is seen in **xerophytes**, which are plants adapted for growing in dry environments.

Xerophytes usually have a number of adaptations to reduce water loss by transpiration and to maximise water uptake from the soil:
- leaves are reduced to spines to minimise the surface area available for transpiration (associated with stems that photosynthesise) — e.g. gorse
- rolled leaves with sunken stomata and a thick cuticle — e.g. marram grass
- root systems that cover a very wide area or penetrate deep into the soil, together with water storage in the leaves — e.g. cacti

Sexual reproduction

Sexual reproduction involves the fusion of male and female **gametes** to produce a zygote. In sexually reproducing organisms the gametes of an individual are **haploid** (contain half the normal number of chromosomes) and are genetically different from each other due to crossing-over and the independent assortment of chromosomes during **meiosis**. As male and female gametes fuse at random during fertilisation (and the male and female parents have different **genotypes**), there will be genetic variation in the **diploid** zygotes produced by sexual reproduction. This variation is important in **evolution**.

(Make sure that you understand the differences between sexual reproduction and **asexual reproduction**, which is reproduction involving the formation of new individuals from a single parent *without* the fusion of gametes. It *is* possible to have sexual reproduction with just one parent — as seen in self-pollination of flowering plants.)

In order to understand sexual reproduction in flowering plants and humans, it is important to know the details of **meiosis**. Meiosis involves two successive divisions of a diploid cell, resulting in the production of haploid gametes. This is summarised in the table below.

Stage	1st division	2nd division
Prophase	Homologous chromosomes form pairs and may exchange genetic material during crossing-over	Individual chromosomes can be seen to consist of a pair of chromatids
Metaphase	Homologous pairs line up at random on the equator of the cell, attached to spindle fibres by their centromeres	Individual chromosomes line up at random on the equator of the cell, attached to spindle fibres by their centromeres
Anaphase	Homologous chromosomes separate and move to opposite ends of the dividing cell	Chromatids separate and move to opposite ends of the dividing cell
Telophase	The first division is completed	The second division is completed and four gametes are produced from the original parent cell

It is vital not to confuse meiosis (reduction division) with **mitosis**, which is a type of cell division used for growth. The words meiosis and mitosis even look similar, so make sure that your spelling is correct. Finally, it is useful to note that the processes involved in the second meiotic division are essentially the same as those seen in mitosis, but with only half the normal number of chromosomes.

Reproduction in flowering plants

In order to understand sexual reproduction in flowering plants, it is important to know the key reproductive structures involved.

Anther — the part of a flower in which pollen develops. The pollen is later released when the anther ruptures.

Carpel — one of the female reproductive organs of a flower. Each carpel consists of a stigma, a style and an ovary, which contains the female gametes.

Flower — a structure that contains the sexual reproductive organs in certain plants. Flowers are found in plants of the phylum Angiospermophyta. They are very variable in form, ranging from the small green flowers found in wind-pollinated plants to large, brightly coloured flowers in plants pollinated by insects or other animals. Pollination must occur if sexual reproduction is to be successful. In other words, pollen has to be transferred from the anther to the stigma of the same or a different flower.

Fruit — the structure that encloses the seeds in a flowering plant. A fruit develops from an ovary after fertilisation in the plant. Its function is to aid dispersal of seeds by animals or mechanical methods.

- **Animal dispersal** — edible fruits (e.g. cherries) are consumed by animals and the undigested seeds pass out in the faeces. Other fruits are sticky or have hooks so that they become temporarily attached to the fur or feathers of a passing mammal or bird.
- **Mechanical dispersal** — many of these fruits are light and often have hairs that increase their surface area, enabling them to be blown by the wind (e.g. dandelions). Other fruits dry out and suddenly split, flinging the seeds over a wide area.

Ovary — an organ that produces female gametes. In plants, each ovary contains a number of ovules, which become seeds following fertilisation. The ovary itself develops into a fruit.

Pollen — a collection of grains containing the male gametes of flowering plants. The exact structure of pollen grains depends upon the species of plant in question. In general, pollen from insect-pollinated plants is textured and relatively large. Pollen from wind-pollinated plants is smaller and lighter, and usually has a smooth texture. (Note that a pollen grain is *not* the male gamete of a flowering plant. It *contains* the male gamete.)

Seed — a structure containing the embryo of a flowering plant. A seed develops from a fertilised ovule. In addition to the embryo, a seed usually contains a food store and has a protective coat known as the testa. Food is stored either in endosperm tissue (e.g. pine seed) or in the cotyledons (e.g. broad bean seed). Seeds are dispersed by one of a number of mechanisms and then usually lie dormant for a period of time. When conditions are favourable, the embryo plant begins to grow. This is known as germination.

Stamen — one of the male reproductive organs of a flower. Each stamen consists of a filament (stalk) and an anther, which produces pollen.

Stigma — the surface at the tip of a carpel in a flower which is adapted to receive pollen. Pollen is transferred to the stigma by wind or insect vectors during pollination. The pollen grains germinate on the stigma, producing pollen tubes, which grow down through the style to the ovule of the flower. This permits the fusion of male and female gametes during fertilisation.

Style — the stalk of a carpel in a flower, located between the stigma and the ovary. The style is elongated in wind-pollinated plants to allow the feathery stigma to hang outside the flower and trap pollen.

The transfer of pollen from an anther to a stigma in flowering plants is known as **pollination**. Self-pollination occurs if pollen is transferred from an anther to a stigma of the same plant. Cross-pollination is the transfer of pollen to the stigma of a different plant of the same species. This is usually achieved by the use of wind or insect vectors.

There are several differences between wind-pollinated and insect-pollinated plants, as summarised by the table below.

Feature	Wind-pollinated	Insect-pollinated
Petals	Absent, or small and not colourful	Large and colourful
Nectar	Absent	Present
Stamens	Hang outside flower	Within flower
Stigmas	Feathery, outside flower	Sticky, inside flower
Pollen	Smaller grains, produced in large amounts, smooth and dry surface	Larger grains, produced in smaller amounts, sticky or rough surface

(Note that pollination is *not* the same as fertilisation, which involves the actual fusion of male and female gametes.)

Three mechanisms are used to ensure cross-pollination (which is advantageous to the plant):
- **dioeciousness** — dioecious (separate sex) plants means cross-pollination is the only option (e.g. holly)
- **protandry** — the condition in which the male reproductive organs of a flower mature before the female reproductive organs (e.g. ivy)
- **protogyny** — the condition in which the female reproductive organs of a flower mature before the male reproductive organs (e.g. buttercup)

Reproduction in humans

The male reproductive organs in humans are the **testes** and the female reproductive organs are the **ovaries**. It is in these organs that **gametogenesis** (the formation of gametes) takes place.

Spermatogenesis is the production of **sperm** by the testes. Certain cells (spermatogonia) within the testes divide by **mitosis** to produce large numbers of potential gametes called primary spermatocytes. The primary spermatocytes then undergo **meiosis** to produce sperm. Spermatogenesis is stimulated by follicle-stimulating hormone (FSH).

Oogenesis is the production of female gametes (**eggs**) by the ovaries. Certain cells (oogonia) within the ovary divide by **mitosis** to produce large numbers of potential gametes called primary oocytes. The primary oocytes then undergo **meiosis** to produce first a secondary oocyte and then an ovum (egg). Oogenesis is stimulated by FSH.

The **menstrual cycle** is the cycle of events associated with ovulation (release of an ovum) and the development and breakdown of the endometrium (lining of the uterus). In humans, the menstrual cycle averages 28 days in length. It is regulated by four hormones, as summarised in the diagram below.

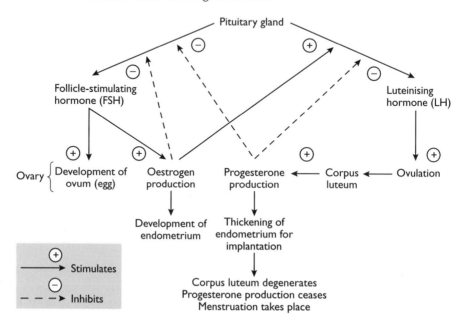

In humans, **fertilisation** involves the fusion of a sperm and an ovum to form a **zygote**. The zygote then develops into an embryo, which becomes embedded in the lining of the uterus during **implantation**. If this occurs, the secretion of progesterone is taken over by the placenta and menstruation does not take place.

The **placenta** is the organ that permits the exchange of materials between a mother and an embryo. It attaches the embryo to the wall of the uterus and is composed of a combination of embryonic and maternal tissues. The placenta allows the exchange of materials between the circulatory systems of the embryo and the mother. It also has an important **endocrine** function, secreting a number of hormones such as progesterone and oestrogen. The placenta is expelled following birth.

Lactation (the production of milk by mammary glands) occurs after birth of the young and is a two-stage process:
- **secretion of milk** — stimulated by the hormone prolactin
- **release of milk** — stimulated by the hormone oxytocin, which is released in response to the sucking action of the infant

Finally, you will be expected to have carried out the following practical work in relation to your work on sexual reproduction:
- an experimental investigation into the factors affecting the growth of pollen grains
- observations of meiosis in preparations of insect testis squash

UNIT 3

Modes of nutrition

This section of the specification requires you to understand the basic principles of different modes of nutrition. These are summarised below.

Autotrophic nutrition — the synthesis of organic molecules from simple inorganic molecules, such as carbon dioxide and water. Autotrophic nutrition requires a source of energy. **Photosynthesis** uses light energy (e.g. green plants) and **chemosynthesis** uses energy derived from chemical reactions (e.g. nitrifying bacteria in soil).

Heterotrophic nutrition — a type of nutrition in which an organism gains its required nutrients by consuming complex organic molecules. All animals, fungi and most bacteria are heterotrophic. There are four types of heterotrophic nutrition: holozoic, saprobiontic, parasitic and mutualistic.

Holozoic nutrition — feeding on organic matter obtained from the bodies of other organisms. Food is digested internally by enzymes and the soluble products of digestion are then absorbed. Herbivores (animals that feed on plants, e.g. sheep) and carnivores (animals that feed on other animals, e.g. dogs) show particular structural adaptations to their diet.

Saprobiontic nutrition — feeding on organic matter from dead and decaying organisms. Food is digested externally by enzymes and the soluble products of digestion are then absorbed. The fungus *Rhizopus* is an example of a saprobiontic organism.

Parasitic nutrition — feeding on organic matter in the living tissues of a host organism. Digestion is not normally required as soluble nutrients can be absorbed directly from the host. The tapeworm *Taenia* is an example of a parasitic organism.

Mutualistic nutrition — a feeding relationship between two different species which results in benefit to both. For example, the bacterium *Rhizobium* has a mutualistic relationship with Papilionaceae (leguminous plants, such as clover, peas or beans).

Ecosystems

There are a number of common terms that you need to understand when learning about ecosystems. These are defined below.

Biosphere — the part of the Earth and its atmosphere inhabited by living organisms. The biosphere is made up of many different ecosystems.

Ecosystem — a stable but dynamic system, characterised by the interaction of its **biotic** (living) and **abiotic** (non-living) components. Ecosystems consist of one or more communities of organisms living in a particular habitat. Each community contains populations of producers, consumers and decomposers, and each population occupies a particular ecological niche within the habitat.

3

Habitat — the particular environment in which an organism lives. A habitat is usually a defined area with characteristic abiotic and biotic conditions.

Producer — an autotrophic organism that forms the first trophic level in a food chain. Most terrestrial food chains are based on green plants, which convert light energy to chemical energy by photosynthesis. Some of this energy is then transferred to primary consumers (herbivores) when the plants are eaten.

Consumer — any of the heterotrophic organisms in a food chain or food web. Herbivores feed on producers (green plants) and are known as primary consumers. Carnivores can be secondary consumers (if they feed on herbivores), or tertiary consumers (if they feed on other carnivores).

Decomposer — an organism that breaks down dead material or waste products. Decomposers and detritivores play an important role in the recycling of nutrients incorporated in the waste or dead remains of plants and animals. Detritivores tend to break up the dead material, providing a large surface area for the action of decomposers.

Trophic level — the position occupied by an organism in a food chain. The first trophic level is occupied by producers, such as green plants. The second trophic level contains primary consumers (herbivores) which feed on the producers. The third trophic level contains secondary consumers (carnivores) which feed on the primary consumers, and so on. There are rarely more than five trophic levels in a food chain as energy is lost during the transfer from one level to the next. The diagram below shows the trophic levels of organisms making up a typical food chain.

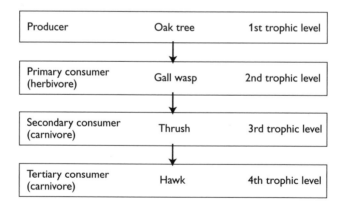

(Note that the ultimate trophic level is that of the decomposers, which release inorganic nutrients for recycling via the producers. One problem with using trophic levels is that many animals feed at more than one trophic level, making it difficult to accurately define feeding relationships.)

Food chain — a sequence of feeding relationships in an environment. Many animals feed at more than one trophic level and also compete with each other for the same food sources. Therefore, single food chains rarely exist and a food web is a more realistic representation of feeding relationships.

Food web — a system of interconnected food chains. A simplified food web is shown below.

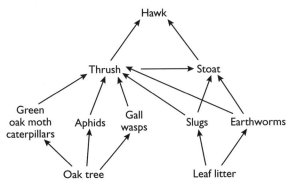

(Note that some animals can feed as both a primary consumer and a secondary consumer. Therefore it is sometimes difficult to define feeding relationships accurately.)

Energy flow

The basis of all energy flow through ecosystems is **photosynthesis**, which is summarised in the following equation:

$$\text{carbon dioxide} + \text{water} \xrightarrow[\text{chlorophyll}]{\text{sunlight}} \text{glucose} + \text{oxygen}$$

In order to be able to describe energy flow accurately, you need to understand the concepts of net productivity and pyramids of number, biomass and energy.

Net productivity is a measure of the rate at which energy is used to form new tissues. Organic molecules accumulate in living organisms by autotrophic or heterotrophic nutrition. The total amount of material accumulated is known as the gross productivity. However, some of this material is used for respiration, and some is lost by excretion and defaecation. Net productivity is the amount of organic material remaining for growth, as summarised by the following equation:

net productivity = gross productivity – (respiration + excretion + defaecation)

Net productivity is normally measured for a particular area over a particular time and in units of energy, for example $kJ\,m^{-2}\,year^{-1}$.

Pyramids of number, biomass and energy are three different ways of describing the relationships between different trophic levels in a food chain.

- A **pyramid of numbers** shows the number of individuals at each trophic level in a food chain.
- A **pyramid of biomass** shows the mass of organisms at each trophic level in a food chain.
- A **pyramid of energy** shows the amount of energy available at each trophic level in a food chain.

The diagram below shows the shape of these pyramids for a simple food chain. Note that the area of the boxes represents the number, biomass or energy.

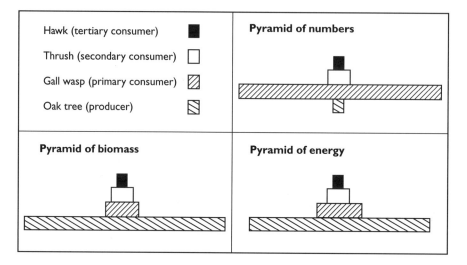

(Note that not all pyramids of numbers have the characteristic upright pyramid shape. The shape varies according to the *size* of the organisms involved.)

You are also expected to have carried out practical work on the estimation of pyramids of numbers and fresh biomass using simple techniques for the collection and determination of fresh mass.

Recycling of nutrients

The key cycles that you need to know and understand are the water cycle, the carbon cycle and the nitrogen cycle.

The water cycle

Water enters the atmosphere by evaporation from rivers, lakes and the sea, and by transpiration. This forms clouds which then release water as rain or snow. The water eventually returns to the sea via streams and rivers. The water cycle is also known as the hydrological cycle.

content guidance

The carbon cycle

The carbon cycle is summarised in the diagram below.

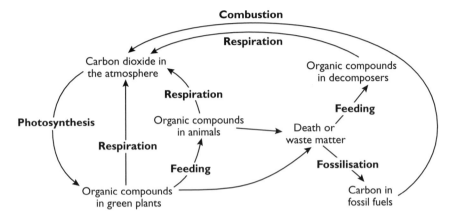

Nitrogen cycle

The nitrogen cycle is summarised in the diagram below.

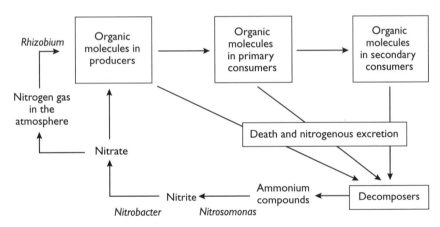

(Note that denitrification and nitrogen fixation are not always involved in the nitrogen cycle.)

Energy resources

This part of the specification requires you to understand how energy resources can be managed in a sustainable manner. This involves conserving energy resources, using the resources more efficiently and seeking alternative (renewable) resources.

Non-renewable energy resources are fossil fuels, such as coal and oil. They are cheap and readily available, but supplies are limited and burning these fuels causes atmospheric pollution.

Renewable energy resources are generally more complex to produce in a useable form and so more expensive than fossil fuels. However, supplies of some of these resources are theoretically unlimited. Examples include fast-growing biomass (e.g. willow), gasohol from sugar, and biogas from domestic and agricultural wastes.

Human influences on the environment

The three main influences of human activity on the environment are **deforestation**, **desertification** and **pollution**.

Deforestation — trees are removed to provide timber and fuel, and to supply agricultural land for crops and animals. Excessive deforestation results in soil erosion, loss of biodiversity and global warming (via the greenhouse effect).

Desertification — grazing animals and gathering fuelwood reduce levels of vegetation in dry areas, leading to soil erosion and salinisation (an increase in salt concentration in the soil). This results in the gradual spread of desert and a reduction in the availability of fertile land.

Pollution — pollution can be defined as a change in the abiotic or biotic characteristics of the environment as a result of human activities. Examples include pollution of the atmosphere and of water supplies.

- **Atmospheric pollution** — the increased production of sulphur dioxide and oxides of nitrogen during the burning of fossil fuels leads to **acid rain** (resulting in damage to aquatic and terrestrial ecosystems, and the erosion of buildings). Carbon dioxide, nitrous oxide, methane, ozone and chlorofluorocarbons (CFCs) in the atmosphere contribute to the **greenhouse effect** and **global warming** (resulting in rising sea levels and a disruption of ecosystems), as summarised below.

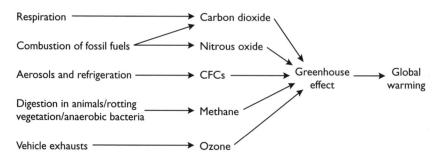

- **Water pollution** — this can be caused by a number of factors, such as the leaching of fertilisers into rivers and lakes, leading to **eutrophication**. Eutrophication is the decrease in biodiversity resulting from the pollution of a river or lake, as summarised below.

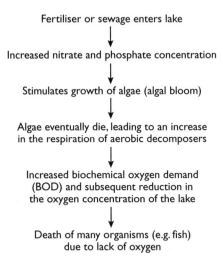

Fertiliser or sewage enters lake

↓

Increased nitrate and phosphate concentration

↓

Stimulates growth of algae (algal bloom)

↓

Algae eventually die, leading to an increase
in the respiration of aerobic decomposers

↓

Increased biochemical oxygen demand
(BOD) and subsequent reduction in
the oxygen concentration of the lake

↓

Death of many organisms (e.g. fish)
due to lack of oxygen

(Note that it is *not* the algal bloom that reduces the oxygen concentration of the water, but the increase in aerobic respiration by the decomposing bacteria.)

Questions
&
Answers

In this section of the guide there are four mock papers written in the same format as the real unit test papers. All questions are based on the topic areas outlined in the Content Guidance section. When you have completed a paper, ideally under timed conditions — allowing 1 hour 15 minutes each for mock papers 1 and 2 (Unit Test 2) and 1 hour each for mock papers 3 and 4 (Unit Test 3) — compare your answers with those of Candidate A and Candidate B. Try to avoid looking at the sample answers and examiner's comments before completing the tests. Make sure that you correct any mistakes and that you study the examiner's comments very carefully. You will get a much better grade if you can avoid the common errors made by many candidates in their unit tests.

Examiner's comments

Candidate responses include examiner's comments after each section of the answer. These examiner's comments are preceded by the icon *e* and indicate where credit is due. In the weaker answers, they also point out areas for improvement, specific problems and common errors, such as poor time management, lack of clarity, weak or non-existent development, irrelevance, misinterpretation of the question and mistaken meanings of terms.

Exchange, transport and reproduction (I)

(1) The table below refers to features of two types of cells present in mammalian blood. If the feature is correct, place a tick (✔) in the appropriate box and if the feature is not correct, place a cross (✖) in the appropriate box.

Feature	Neutrophil	Erythrocyte
Contains haemoglobin		
Has a lobed nucleus		
Produces antibodies		
Capable of phagocytosis		

4 marks

(2) Read the following passage about transpiration and then write on the dotted lines the most appropriate word or words to complete the passage.

Transpiration occurs mainly through the .... on leaves, but also to a lesser extent through the .... on woody stems. This loss of water vapour creates a water potential gradient which draws water up the .... tissue according to the cohesion–tension theory. The rate of transpiration is increased by .... and ....

5 marks

(3) The table below summarises the stages of the cardiac cycle. Complete the table by writing the name of the stage, the pressure in the atria and ventricles (high or low), or the position of the atrioventricular and semilunar valves (open or closed) in the boxes provided.

Stage	Atrial pressure	Ventricular pressure	Atrioventricular valves	Semilunar valves
	High	Low	Open	Closed
Ventricular systole			Closed	Open
Atrial diastole	Low	Low		
			Open	Closed

5 marks

(4) The diagram below shows a longitudinal section of two cells of phloem tissue in a plant stem.

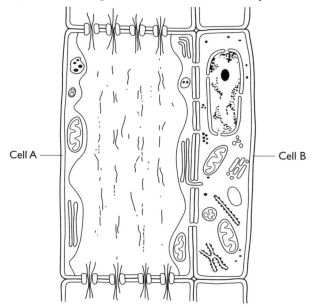

Cell A —

Cell B —

(a) Name the cells labelled **A** and **B** in the diagram. (2 marks)

(b) Name *one* other type of cell found in phloem tissue. (1 mark)

(c) Explain the function of phloem tissue in a plant. (3 marks)

Total: 6 marks

(5) The flow chart below describes the regulation of the menstrual cycle by hormones in a human female.

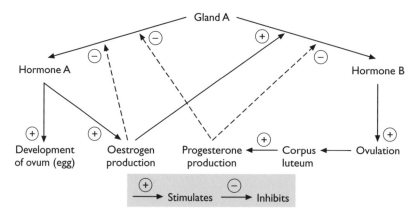

(a) Name gland **A**. (1 mark)

(b) Identify the hormones labelled **A** and **B** in the flow chart. (2 marks)

(c) Where does oestrogen production take place? (1 mark)

(d) State *one* effect of an increase in the concentration of oestrogen in the blood. (1 mark)

(e) The 'combined pill' is an oral contraceptive pill containing both oestrogen and progesterone. Using the information in the diagram, explain how this pill prevents pregnancy. (3 marks)

Total: 8 marks

(6) The diagram below shows the structure of a mature pollen grain.

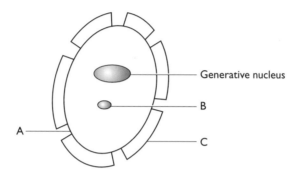

(a) Name the structures labelled **A, B** and **C** on the diagram. (3 marks)

The formation of pollen grains is summarised in the diagram below.

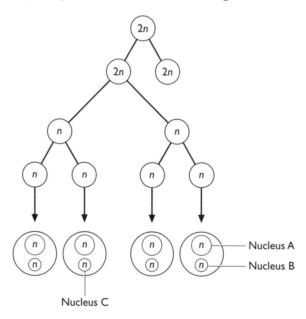

(b) Explain how the processes of cell division result in:
   (i) the nuclei labelled **A** and **B** being genetically identical (2 marks)
   (ii) the nuclei labelled **B** and **C** being genetically different (4 marks)

Total: 9 marks

(7) The diagram below shows a simple respirometer. It is being used to measure the rate of oxygen uptake by germinating peas in tube B. There are no peas in tube A. The syringe in tube B can be used to level the fluid in the manometer.

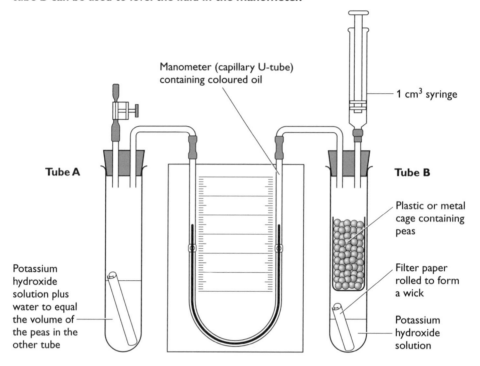

(a) (i) What is the purpose of the potassium hydroxide in tube B? (1 mark)

(ii) Explain how tube A acts as an experimental control. (3 marks)

(iii) Explain how the respirometer can be used to measure the rate of oxygen uptake by the peas. (4 marks)

The table below shows the readings that were obtained in this experiment over a period of 40 minutes.

Time/minutes	Syringe reading/mm^3
0	0
10	5.2
20	8.0
30	11.3
40	14.2

(b) Use the information in the table to calculate the respiratory rate of the germinating peas. Show your working. (3 marks)

Total: 11 marks

(8) The graph below shows the oxygen dissociation curve of human haemoglobin at low and high partial pressures of carbon dioxide.

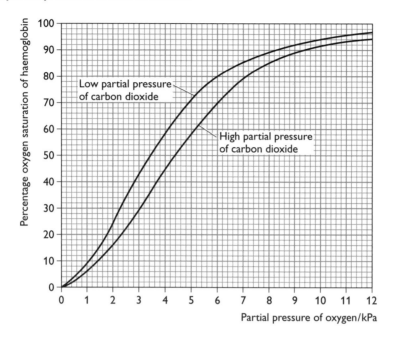

(a) Explain how the shape of the dissociation curve at a low partial pressure of carbon dioxide is related to the ability of haemoglobin to transport oxygen from the lungs to respiring tissues. (3 marks)

(b) From the graph, find the percentage saturation of haemoglobin in blood from an area of the body where the partial pressure of carbon dioxide is high and the partial pressure of oxygen is 6 kPa. (1 mark)

(c) Blood that is fully (100%) saturated with oxygen carries 105 cm³ of oxygen in 1 litre of blood. Calculate the volume of oxygen released when 1 litre of blood which has become 80% saturated at a low partial pressure of carbon dioxide reaches a part of the body where the partial pressure of carbon dioxide is high and the partial pressure of oxygen is 6 kPa. Show your working. (3 marks)

(d) (i) What term is used to describe the effect of carbon dioxide upon the oxygen dissociation curve? (1 mark)

   (ii) Suggest how this effect might be advantageous in humans. (2 marks)

(e) On the graph, draw the oxygen dissociation curve for fetal haemoglobin at a low partial pressure of carbon dioxide. (2 marks)

Total: 12 marks

(9) Give an account of the digestion and absorption of carbohydrates by a human. **10 marks**

Exchange, transport and reproduction (II)

(1) The table below refers to features of wind-pollinated and insect-pollinated plants. If the feature is correct, place a tick (✔) in the appropriate box and if the feature is not correct, place a cross (✖) in the appropriate box.

Feature	Wind-pollinated	Insect-pollinated
Large and colourful petals		
Nectar present		
Stamens usually hang outside the flower		
Stigmas usually sticky and inside the flower		

4 marks

(2) The diagram below shows a transverse section of a young, dicotyledonous root.

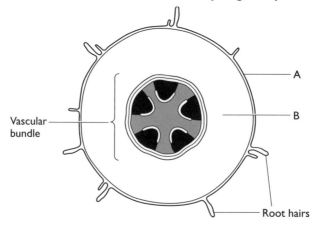

Vascular bundle

A

B

Root hairs

(a) Name the tissues labelled **A** and **B** in the diagram. (2 marks)

(b) Water moves across a root by one of three pathways. Complete the table below by writing the name of the pathway next to its description.

Pathway	Description
	The route by which water travels through the cytoplasm and plasmodesmata of plant cells.
	The route by which water travels through the vacuoles of plant cells.
	The route by which water travels through the cell walls of a plant.

(3 marks)

Total: 5 marks

(3) The diagram below shows a transverse section through a villus.

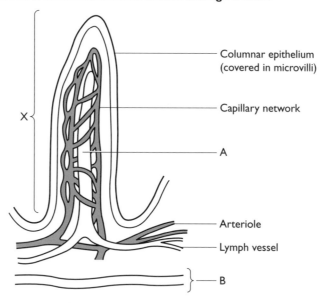

(a) (i) Name the parts labelled **A** and **B** on the diagram.   (2 marks)

(ii) **Which of the following figures is the most likely to be correct for distance X on the diagram (underline your answer).**   (1 mark)

10 μm   100 μm   1 mm   10 mm   100 mm

(b) State **two** ways in which a villus is adapted for its function of absorption.   (2 marks)

Total: 5 marks

(4) The diagram below shows alternation of generations in the basic plant life cycle.

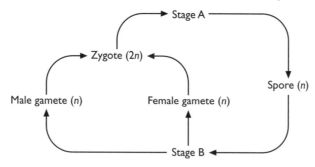

(a) (i) Name stages **A** and **B** on the diagram.   (2 marks)

(ii) Label the diagram with an **X** at the point where meiosis occurs.   (1 mark)

(b) Explain how meiosis leads to genetic variation.   (3 marks)

Total: 6 marks

(5) (a) Explain what is meant by the term *transpiration*. (2 marks)

The diagram below shows a layer of cells on the underside of a leaf.

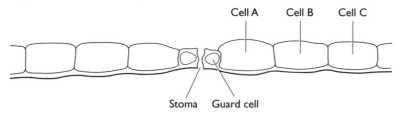

(b) Name the layer of cells shown in the diagram. (1 mark)

The table below shows the concentration of potassium ions in some of the cells shown in the diagram when the stoma is open and when the stoma is closed.

Cell	Concentration of potassium ions/arbitrary units	
	Stoma open	Stoma closed
Guard cell	224	47
Cell A	147	78
Cell B	49	99
Cell C	36	222

(c) (i) Describe the changes that take place in the concentrations of potassium ions in cells A, B and C when the stoma closes. (2 marks)
(ii) Explain how the changes in potassium ion concentration are related to the mechanism for the closing of the stoma. (3 marks)

Total: 8 marks

(6) A typical electrocardiogram (ECG) for a healthy adult human is known as a PQRST wave, as shown below.

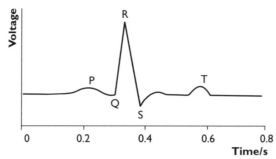

(a) Describe what is represented by the following parts of the wave:
(i) the peak at P
(ii) the QRS complex
(iii) the peak at T (3 marks)

The diagram below shows the single circulation system found in fish.

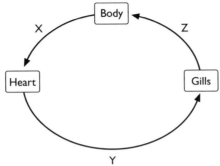

(b) At which stage, **X, Y** or **Z**, is:
  (i) the pressure at its highest
  (ii) the oxygen concentration at its highest   (2 marks)
(c) Compare the single circulation system found in a fish with the double
    circulation system found in mammals.   (3 marks)

                                  Total: 8 marks

(7) An experiment was carried out with cells of potato tissue to determine the effect of temperature on the absorption of sodium ions.

Slices of potato tissue were placed in sodium chloride solution of known concentration. The changes in concentration of sodium ions in the solution were determined at 30 minute intervals for 4 hours. From these measurements, the mass of sodium ions taken in by the potato cells was determined. The experiment was carried out at 10°C and 25°C and the results are shown in the graph below.

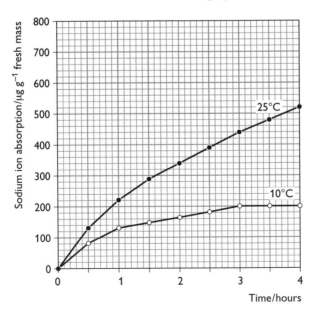

(a) State *three* ways in which sodium ions can be taken up by cells. (3 marks)

(b) Calculate the mean rate of absorption of sodium at 25°C between 1 and 3 hours. Show your working. (3 marks)

(c) Compare the rates of absorption of sodium ions at 10°C and 25°C during this experiment. (3 marks)

(d) Suggest an explanation for the differences in the rates of absorption of sodium ions at the two temperatures. (3 marks)

Total: 12 marks

(8) The graphs below show the effects of changes in the concentration of respiratory gases in the air on the volume of air inhaled per minute by a person.

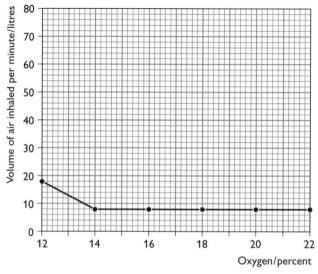

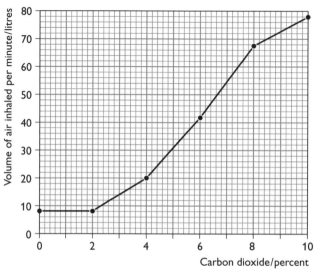

(a) (i) Describe the effect of changing the *oxygen* concentration on the volume
of air inhaled per minute. (2 marks)

(ii) Describe the effect of changing the *carbon dioxide* concentration on the
volume of air inhaled per minute. (2 marks)

(iii) Calculate the percentage increase in the volume of air inhaled per minute
when the concentration of carbon dioxide increases from 3% to 8%.
Show your working. (3 marks)

(b) Describe how an increase in the concentration of carbon dioxide in the blood
might result in an increase in the volume of air inhaled per minute. (3 marks)

The table below shows the percentage of gases in samples of inspired and expired air.

Gas	Inspired air/percent	Expired air/percent
Oxygen	20.67	15.98
Carbon dioxide	0.04	3.90
Nitrogen	78.66	74.76
Water vapour	0.63	5.36

(c) Using the information in the table, explain why the percentage of nitrogen is
lower in expired air than in inspired air. (2 marks)

Total: 12 marks

(9) Give an account of the structural and physiological adaptations shown by
invertebrates to the varying oxygen concentrations found in fresh water.

10 marks

Answers to mock paper 1: Candidate A

(1)

Feature	Neutrophil	Erythrocyte
Contains haemoglobin	✗	✔
Has a lobed nucleus	✔	✗
Produces antibodies	✔ *✗*	✗
Capable of phagocytosis	✗ *✗*	✗

🖉 This response earns 2 out of 4 marks. Candidate A appears to know that neutrophils are white blood cells. However, neutrophils do *not* produce antibodies and they *are* capable of phagocytosis. The candidate has probably confused neutrophils with lymphocytes (another type of white blood cell), which *do* produce antibodies but are *not* capable of phagocytosis.

(2) Transpiration occurs mainly through the ......stomata ✔..... on leaves, but also to a lesser extent through the .....lenticels ✔..... on woody stems. This loss of water vapour creates a water potential gradient which draws water up the .....xylem ✔..... tissue according to the cohesion–tension theory. The rate of transpiration is increased by .....temperature *✗*..... and .....humidity *✗*.....

🖉 This answer is worth 3 out of 5 marks. Although temperature and humidity *do* affect the rate of transpiration, the last two answers are not specific enough. It is important to be specific in this case, as a *lower* temperature or a *higher* humidity would *decrease* the rate of transpiration. Therefore the correct answers are **higher temperature** and **lower humidity**.

(3)

Stage	Atrial pressure	Ventricular pressure	Atrioventricular valves	Semilunar valves	
Atrial systole ✔	High	Low	Open	Closed	
Ventricular systole	High	Low	Closed	Open	✗
Atrial diastole	Low	Low	Open	Closed	✔
Ventricular diastole ✔	Low	Low	Open	Closed	✔

🖉 This response is worth 4 out of 5 marks. The only mistake is in the second line. During ventricular systole, the atria are relaxing (so the pressure is *low*) and the ventricles are contracting (so the pressure is *high*).

(4) (a) A = companion cell ✗; B = sieve tube element ✗

🖉 Both of these cells are present, but Candidate A has mixed them up! A is a sieve tube element and B is a companion cell. Note that companion cells possess a nucleus and sieve tube elements do not.

(b) Phloem parenchyma ✓

(c) Phloem tissue transports organic solutes ✓ from the leaves ✓ for use in other parts of the plant which do not photosynthesise, such as the root ✓.

🖉 Full marks for parts (b) and (c). Candidate A scores 4 out of 6 marks for this question.

(5) (a) Thyroid gland ✗

🖉 Gland A is the **pituitary gland**.

(b) A = follicle-stimulating hormone ✓; B = luteinising hormone ✓

(c) In the ovum ✗

🖉 The ovum (egg) itself does *not* produce oestrogen. This hormone is produced by the tissues of the ovary.

(d) It stimulates the production of luteinising hormone ✓.

🖉 This is one correct answer. Another possible response could be that **it stimulates the development of the endometrium**.

(e) It stops the production of eggs ✓.

🖉 This response is only worth 1 mark out of 3. Candidate A has not explained *how* the production of eggs (ova) is prevented, i.e. by inhibition of the production of follicle-stimulating hormone from the pituitary gland. The candidate has also not referred to the effect of progesterone in the pill. **Progesterone inhibits the production of LH and so prevents ovulation.** Overall, Candidate A receives 4 out of 8 marks for this question.

(6) (a) A = exine ✗; B = endosperm ✗; C = intine ✗

🖉 This answer is worth no marks. Candidate A has mixed up the intine (thin inner wall) with the exine (thick outer wall) and has incorrectly identified structure B as endosperm tissue. Endosperm is a nutritious tissue found in the *seeds* of flowering plants. Structure B is the **pollen tube nucleus**.

(b) (i) The nuclei labelled A and B are produced by mitosis of the parent cell ✓.

🖉 This is correct, but only worth 1 out of 2 marks. Candidate A has not explained that **mitosis results in identical copies of the genetic material being passed on from the parent cell**.

(ii) The nuclei labelled B and C are genetically different because their parent cells are genetically different ✓. This is because the parent cells are produced by meiosis ✓ and meiosis leads to genetic variation due to independent assortment of homologous chromosomes ✓ and chiasma between the chromosomes ✓.

🖉 This is a good answer, earning 4 out of 4 marks. Overall, Candidate A scores 5 out of 9 marks for this question.

(7) (a) (i) To absorb oxygen ✗

🖉 This is incorrect. If the potassium hydroxide absorbed oxygen, we would not be able to measure oxygen uptake by the seeds! The purpose of the potassium hydroxide in tube B is to **absorb carbon dioxide**.

(ii) It has the same conditions as tube B, except for the peas ✗.

🖉 The student has not understood the purpose of tube A. This tube acts as a **thermobarometer**, which **compensates for small changes in temperature or pressure in the respirometer**. This is important because **gas volumes are affected by changes in temperature and pressure** and so tube A is needed if we require accurate results.

(iii) The peas take in oxygen and give out carbon dioxide ✓. The carbon dioxide is absorbed by the potassium hydroxide and so the volume of gas falls ✓. This volume is equal to the amount of oxygen used ✓.

🖉 This answer is worth 3 out of 4 marks. It does not state *how* the decrease in gas volume is measured, or how this is used to calculate the *rate* of oxygen uptake. The syringe can be used to level the fluid in the manometer and the volume of air added is equal to the volume of oxygen used. Furthermore, the volume of oxygen used per unit time provides a measure of the rate of oxygen uptake by the peas.

(b) The respiratory rate is: $\frac{14.2}{40}$ ✓ $= 0.355$ ✓

🖉 The calculation is correct, but the student has forgotten to put in the units (mm^3 oxygen min^{-1}), and therefore scores 2 out of 3 marks. Overall, this answer earns 5 out of 11 marks.

(8) (a) The blood is rapidly saturated with oxygen in the lungs because pO_2 is high ✓ and it loses the oxygen in respiring tissues because the pO_2 is low ✓.

🖉 This is correct, but only worth 2 out of 3 marks because Candidate A has not related the answer to *the shape of the curve*. The candidate should have stated that **the steep rise of the curve at low partial pressures of oxygen indicates that a small change in pO_2 results in a relatively large change in the saturation of haemoglobin with oxygen.**

(b) 80% ✗

🖉 This is incorrect. It looks like Candidate A has read off the answer from the curve at where the partial pressure of carbon dioxide is *low*. The correct answer is **70%**.

(c) The percentage saturation of blood when the partial pressure of carbon dioxide is high and the partial pressure of oxygen is 6 kPa = 80%. Blood which is 80% saturated will contain (80/100) × 105 = 84 cm^3 of oxygen ✓ but no oxygen will be released because there is no change in the percentage saturation of the blood.

This answer only receives 1 out of 3 marks because Candidate A found the wrong value in part (b). However, the reasoning is correct and a second mark might be awarded. The fact that the percentage saturation does not seem to have changed should have given the student a clue that a mistake had been made in part (b). The correct answer can be seen in Candidate B's response to this question.

(d) (i) The Bohr shift ✓

(ii) An increase in the concentration of carbon dioxide causes the curve to shift to the right, causing haemoglobin to release less oxygen ✗. Therefore, in actively respiring tissues, where the concentration of carbon dioxide in the blood is high, haemoglobin will contain more oxygen ✗.

*There is some confusion here. A shift to the right makes haemoglobin release **more** oxygen. This is important for rapidly respiring tissues as the **haemoglobin will release its oxygen to the tissues**. The tissues cannot get the oxygen if it is tightly bound to haemoglobin!*

(e)

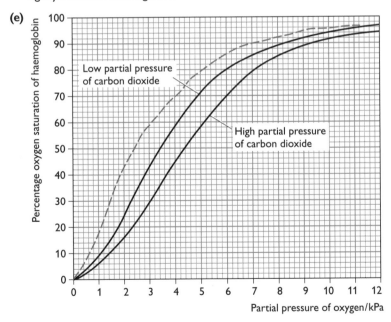

*This answer is correct. The curve is on the **left** of the adult haemoglobin curve (with approximately the same start and end points). This is because fetal haemoglobin must have a higher affinity for oxygen than adult haemoglobin in order to take oxygen from the mother's blood across the placenta. Overall, Candidate A scores 6 out of 12 marks for this question.*

(9) Some digestion starts in the mouth, where salivary amylase ✓ in saliva breaks down starch into glucose. Cellulose is then digested by pepsin in the stomach. Lactose from milk is broken down to glucose and galactose ✓ in the small intestine by lactase ✓. The glucose is then absorbed into the blood ✓.

> This is a very limited (and confused) answer, worth only 4 out of 10 marks. Salivary amylase breaks down starch to **dextrins** (short chains of glucose molecules) and **maltose**, *not* directly to glucose. Cellulose is not digested at all by humans and pepsin is an enzyme that digests **proteins**. Remember that *no* carbohydrate digestion takes place in the stomach. Other points that could have been made are: **mechanical digestion by the teeth and gut muscles; further breakdown of starch by pancreatic amylase in the duodenum;** the action of other enzymes, such as **maltase (digests maltose to glucose)** or **sucrase (digests sucrose to glucose and fructose)**; and further details about absorption.

Overall, Candidate A scores 37 out of 70 for this mock paper, which would be a grade D.

Answers to mock paper 1: Candidate B

(1)

Feature	Neutrophil	Erythrocyte
Contains haemoglobin	✗	✔
Has a lobed nucleus	✔	✗
Produces antibodies	✔ ✗	✗
Capable of phagocytosis	✔	✗

> ✐ This response earns 3 out of 4 marks. Candidate B appears to know that erythrocytes are red blood cells and neutrophils are white blood cells. However, neutrophils do *not* produce antibodies. Antibodies are produced by lymphocytes, which are another type of white blood cell.

(2) Transpiration occurs mainly through the ......stomata ✓..... on leaves, but also to a lesser extent through the .....lenticels ✓..... on woody stems. This loss of water vapour creates a water potential gradient which draws water up the .....phloem ✗..... tissue according to the cohesion–tension theory. The rate of transpiration is increased by .....higher temperature ✓..... and .....lower humidity ✓.....

> ✐ This answer is worth 4 out of 5 marks. Water moves through the plant in the **xylem** tissue, not the phloem.

(3)

Stage	Atrial pressure	Ventricular pressure	Atrioventricular valves	Semilunar valves
Atrial systole ✓	High	Low	Open	Closed
Ventricular systole	Low	High ✓	Closed	Open
Atrial diastole	Low	Low	Closed	Open ✗
Ventricular diastole ✓	Low	Low ✓	Open	Closed

> ✐ This response is worth 4 out of 5 marks. Candidate B obviously knows the stages of the cardiac cycle and can identify them from the information given. He or she also knows that when the atria or ventricles are contracting (systole), the pressure is high and that when they are relaxing (diastole), the pressure is low. The only mistake is in the third line. When the atria (and ventricles) are relaxed and filling with blood, the atrioventricular valves are *open* and the semilunar valves are *closed*.

(4) (a) A = sieve tube element ✓; B = companion cell ✓

(b) Phloem parenchyma ✓

(c) Phloem tissue transports organic solutes ✓ from their sites of synthesis (by photosynthesis) in the leaves ✓ for use in other parts of the plant, such as for cell division or active transport in the root ✓.

🖉 An excellent answer, worth full marks.

(5) (a) Pituitary gland ✓

(b) A = luteinising hormone ✗; B = follicle-stimulating hormone ✗

🖉 This is a fairly common mistake, confusing the two hormones produced by the pituitary gland. Remember that FSH (labelled A) stimulates the development of the ovum and oestrogen production, and LH (labelled B) stimulates ovulation and the production of progesterone.

(c) In the ovary ✓

(d) It stimulates the development of the endometrium ✓.

🖉 This answer is correct. Another possible response could be that **it stimulates the production of LH**.

(e) Oestrogen inhibits FSH production ✓ preventing the development of an ovum ✓.

🖉 This response is worth 2 marks out of 3. The student has not referred to the effect of progesterone in the pill. **Progesterone inhibits the production of LH and so prevents ovulation.** Progesterone also inhibits FSH production and a 'progesterone only' pill would also be effective. Overall, Candidate B receives 5 out of 8 marks for this question.

(6) (a) A = intine ✓; B = pollen tube nucleus ✓; C = exine ✓

(b) (i) The nuclei labelled A and B are produced by mitosis of the parent cell ✓. This type of nuclear division results in identical copies of the genetic material ✓.

(ii) The nuclei labelled B and C are genetically different because their parent cells are genetically different ✓. This is because the parent cells are produced by meiosis ✓.

🖉 The answer to part (b)(ii) is correct, but only earns 2 out of 4 marks. This is because insufficient detail has been supplied; only two points have been made. The student should have gone on to explain *how* meiosis produces genetically different cells, i.e. by **independent assortment of homologous chromosomes** and **crossing-over between homologous chromosomes**. Make sure that you make a valid biological point for each mark. Overall, Candidate B scores 7 out of 9 marks for this question.

(7) (a) (i) To absorb carbon dioxide ✓

(ii) Tube A acts as a barometer ✓. It compensates for small changes in pressure in the respirometer ✓ to avoid changes in gas volume due to changes in pressure ✓.

(iii) As the peas respire they take in oxygen and give out carbon dioxide ✓. The carbon dioxide is absorbed by the potassium hydroxide and so the volume of gas falls ✓. This causes the fluid level in the manometer to rise on the right-hand side ✓. After a period of time, the syringe can be used to level the fluid in the manometer and the volume of air added is equal to the volume of oxygen used ✓(MAX). The volume of oxygen used per unit time provides a measure of the rate of oxygen uptake by the peas.

🖉 An excellent answer, earning full marks. Note that there are usually more points available on the marking scheme than the question is actually worth. You do not need to get *all* the points to get full marks — just 4 points in this case. The examiner has written MAX after 4 points have been awarded, even though the answer continues. The last point *would* be worth a mark, but the student has already achieved the maximum. This tends to happen more often in free-prose questions.

(b) 14.2 mm^3 of oxygen has been used in 40 minutes. Therefore the respiratory rate is: $\dfrac{14.2}{40}$ ✓ $= 0.355$ ✓ mm^3 oxygen min^{-1} ✓.

🖉 A very good answer from Candidate B. Overall, this answer earns **11 out of 11 marks**.

(8) (a) The steep rise of the curve at low partial pressures of oxygen indicates that a small change in pO_2 results in a relatively large change in the saturation of haemoglobin with oxygen ✓. Therefore in the lungs, where the pO_2 is high, the blood is rapidly saturated with oxygen ✓. Similarly, in rapidly respiring tissues, where the pO_2 is low, oxygen is released from haemoglobin for use by the tissues ✓.

🖉 An excellent answer, worth 3 out of 3 marks.

(b) 71% ✓

🖉 For questions like these, examiners will usually accept any answer within a small range. In this case, any value in the 70–71% range would be marked correct.

(c) The percentage saturation of blood when the partial pressure of carbon dioxide is high and the partial pressure of oxygen is 6 kPa = 71%. Blood that is 80% saturated will contain $(80/100) \times 105 = 84$ cm^3 of oxygen ✓ and blood which is 71% saturated will contain $(71/100) \times 105 = 74.55$ cm^3 of oxygen ✓. Therefore, the volume of oxygen released is $84 - 74.55 = 9.45$ cm^3 ✓.

🖉 A perfect answer to a complicated question. Note that the first value needed comes from the answer to part (b). The student has set out the calculation very carefully, showing every step. It is important always to show your working.

(d) (i) The Bohr shift ✓
  (ii) An increase in the concentration of carbon dioxide causes the curve to shift to the right, causing haemoglobin to release more oxygen ✓; therefore, in actively respiring tissues, where the concentration of carbon dioxide in the blood is high, haemoglobin readily releases its oxygen to the tissues that need it ✓.

(e)

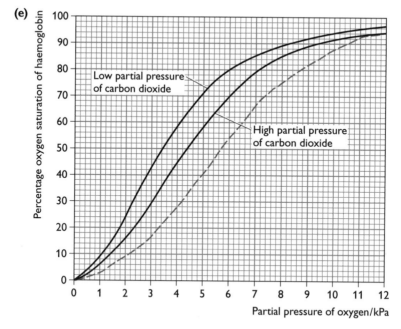

Percentage oxygen saturation of haemoglobin

Low partial pressure of carbon dioxide

High partial pressure of carbon dioxide

Partial pressure of oxygen/kPa

This answer is incorrect. The curve should be drawn to the *left* of the adult haemoglobin curve (with approximately the same start and end points). This is because fetal haemoglobin must have a *higher* affinity for oxygen than adult haemoglobin in order to take oxygen from the mother's blood across the placenta. Overall, Candidate B scores 10 out of 12 marks for this question.

(9) Carbohydrate digestion in humans begins in the mouth. The chewing action of the teeth breaks up the food by mechanical digestion ✓ mixing it with saliva, which contains the enzyme salivary amylase ✓. This enzyme breaks starch down into dextrins (short chains of glucose molecules) and maltose ✓ although the food does not remain in the mouth long enough for much digestion to take place. Starch is broken down further in the duodenum ✓ by pancreatic amylase ✓. In the ileum, the disaccharides maltose, lactose and sucrose are broken down by maltase, lactase and sucrase respectively ✓ into the monosaccharide products of digestion (glucose, galactose and fructose) ✓. Monosaccharides are absorbed mostly in the ileum ✓ by diffusion and active transport ✓ into the blood ✓.

An excellent answer — concise and detailed, with virtually no irrelevant material. More detail could have been provided about absorption, but full marks are still deserved.

Overall, Candidate B scores 60 out of 70 marks for this mock paper, which would be a grade A.

Answers to mock paper 2: Candidate A

(1)

Feature	Wind-pollinated	Insect-pollinated
Large and colourful petals	✗	✔
Nectar present	✗	✔
Stamens usually hang outside the flower	✗ ✗	✔ ✗
Stigmas usually sticky and inside the flower	✔ ✗	✗ ✗

This answer receives 2 out of 4 marks. Candidate A may have confused the stamens (which produce pollen) with the stigmas (which receive pollen). Remember that the structures associated with reproduction are usually found Inside the flower in Insect-pollinated plants (and outside in wind-pollinated plants).

(2) (a) A = endodermis ✗; B = lumen ✗

*Tissue A is the **epidermis** because it is the *outer* layer of cells. The endodermis is a layer of cells found *within* a structure, such as that surrounding the vascular tissue in the root. Tissue B is the **cortex**. A lumen is an empty space within a vessel or tube, such as the lumen of an artery, or of the small intestine.*

(b)

Pathway	Description
Symplast ✓	The route by which water travels through the cytoplasm and plasmodesmata of plant cells.
Vacuolar ✓	The route by which water travels through the vacuoles of plant cells.
Apoplast ✓	The route by which water travels through the cell walls of a plant.

Full marks for part (b). Overall, Candidate A scores 3 out of 5 marks for this question.

(3) (a) (i) A = blood vessel ✗; B = muscle ✓

*Structure A is a **lacteal**, which transports fatty acids and glycerol.*

(ii) 1 mm ✓

(b) There are lots of them and each one has a large surface area ✓.

*This is just about worth 1 mark, although it is a little vague. The question refers to a *single* villus, so the comment about 'lots of them' is not really relevant. Candidate A should also have said *why* a villus has a large surface area (due to the presence of many **microvilli**) and given an additional point, such as **it has a good blood supply to transport away the absorbed products**. Overall, Candidate A scores 3 marks out of 5 for this question.*

(4) (a) (i) A = gametophyte ✗; B = sporophyte ✗

📝 It is easy to confuse these two stages. Note that the product of stage A is a spore, so this stage must be a sporophyte. Likewise, the products of stage B are gametes, so this is a gametophyte.

(ii)

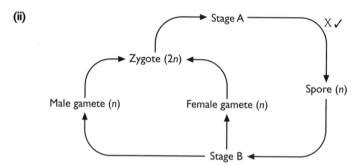

(b) It mixes up the genes, so everyone is different ✗.

📝 This is not incorrect, but it is *very* vague and certainly not worth 3 marks. A better answer would be that, during meiosis, the **homologous chromosomes exchange genetic material by crossing over at chiasmata**. The chromosomes also show **independent assortment**, which means that **gametes are genetically different** from each other and so there will be genetic variation in the next generation. A poor answer to part (b) gives Candidate A only 1 out of 6 marks for this question.

(5) (a) The loss of water vapour from a plant ✓.

📝 Although this is correct, it is a little brief for 2 marks. The student could have been more specific about *where* the water loss occurs, i.e. from **stomata on leaves** and through **lenticels on woody stems**.

(b) The epidermis ✓

📝 This is correct, although (to be specific) most stomata are found on the *lower* epidermis of the leaf.

(c) (i) The concentration of potassium ions falls in cell A, but rises in B and C ✓.

📝 This is correct, but only worth 1 mark. Where possible you should try to indicate the *extent* of the changes by using the numerical data, i.e. state that the concentration falls by 69 arbitrary units in cell A, but rises by 50 and 186 units in cells B and C respectively.

(ii) Potassium ions move out of the guard cells ✓ causing them to become flaccid and so closing the stoma ✓.

📝 This is just about worth 2 marks. A better answer would explain *why* the potassium ions diffuse out of the guard cells (stomata are kept open by the active transport of hydrogen ions out of the guard cells; when this process stops, hydrogen ions diffuse into the guard cells, causing potassium ions to diffuse out) and *how* this causes the guard cells to become flaccid (the water potential in the guard cells increases and so water moves out by osmosis). Overall, Candidate A scores 5 marks out of 8 for this question.

(6) (a) (i) P = ventricles contracting ✗

(ii) QRS = atria contracting ✗

(iii) T = atria and ventricles relaxing ✓

🖉 Candidate A has confused the sequence of events in the cardiac cycle. P represents the contraction of the atria and QRS represents the contraction of the ventricles. Remember, the **A**tria contract before the **V**entricles (A is before V in the alphabet).

(b) (i) Z ✗

(ii) Y ✗

🖉 No marks are awarded for part (b). The pressure is highest just after leaving the heart (Y) and the oxygen concentration is highest just after leaving the gills (Z).

(c) In a single circulation system, the blood passes through the heart only once as it travels around the body. This is not very efficient as a great deal of pressure is lost passing through the gas-exchange surface (gills), so the blood moves very slowly around the rest of the body ✓. In a double circulation system, the blood passes through the heart twice as it travels around the body. This is more efficient as the pressure is increased after the gas-exchange surface (lungs) ✓ by returning to the heart to be pumped to the rest of the body ✓.

🖉 An excellent answer to part (c) gives Candidate A 4 out of 8 marks for the question.

(7) (a) Diffusion ✓; facilitated diffusion ✓; exocytosis ✗

🖉 This answer is worth 2 out of 3 marks. Exocytosis is a mechanism by which substances (usually relatively large proteins) move *out* of cells. The correct third answer is **active transport**.

(b) 440 − 220 = 220 ✓

🖉 Candidate A has correctly interpolated the figures from the graph, but has made two mistakes. The *mean rate* of absorption must be expressed per hour, so (as this is a 2 hour period) 220 must be divided by 2 to give 110. The second mistake was leaving out the units, so the correct answer is **110 µg g^{-1} hour^{-1}.**

(c) The rate of uptake at 25°C is faster than at 10°C ✓. The final mass taken up at 25°C is three times greater than at 10°C ✓. The graph levels off at 10°C.

🖉 This is worth 2 out of 3 marks. The final point is *not* comparative, as it does not say what happens to the graph at 25°C (it keeps rising). Remember, when asked to *compare* A and B, you must say 'In A this happens, but in B something else happens'.

(d) Diffusion is faster at 25°C ✓. Active transport is faster at 25°C ✓.

🖉 This answer earns Candidate A 2 out of 3 marks. The third mark would be awarded for saying *why* diffusion is faster at the higher temperature (an increase in **kinetic energy**) or *why* active transport is faster at the higher temperature (an increase in the **rate of respiration**). Overall, Candidate A scores 7 out of 12 marks for this question.

(8) (a) (i) As it increases, the volume of air inhaled per minute decreases ✓.

🖉 This is just about worth 1 mark. Between 12% and 14% oxygen, the volume of air inhaled *does* decrease as oxygen concentration increases, but above 14% oxygen there is *no change* in the volume of air inhaled.

(ii) As it increases, the volume of air inhaled per minute also increases ✓.

🖉 Again, this is only (just) worth 1 mark. Between 0% and 2% carbon dioxide, there is *no change* in the volume of air inhaled, but above 2% carbon dioxide, the volume of air inhaled *increases* as carbon dioxide concentration *increases*.

(iii) At 3% CO_2, volume of air breathed per minute = 14 litres and at 8% CO_2, volume of air breathed per minute = 68 litres ✓. So the percentage increase = $[(68 - 14)/14] \times 100$ ✓ = 385.7% ✓.

🖉 A very clear answer, worth full marks.

(b) The increase in carbon dioxide in the blood is detected by chemoreceptors ✓ which send signals to the lungs to increase the ventilation rate ✓.

🖉 This answer earns 2 out of 3 marks. The third mark would be awarded for stating *where* the chemoreceptors are located (in the aorta, carotid artery and medulla oblongata in the brain).

(c) The nitrogen has been used in the body to make proteins ✗.

🖉 This is incorrect. Nitrogen gas is *not* used in the body and the *amount* of nitrogen in the air has not actually changed. The increase in water vapour in expired air means that the *percentage* of that air which is nitrogen has fallen. Overall, Candidate A earns 7 out of 12 marks for this question.

(9) An *Amoeba* has a large surface area-to-volume ratio ✓ enabling it to take up oxygen by simple diffusion ✓. Bigger animals, like *Planaria*, have flattened bodies to increase the surface area-to-volume ratio, so they can still use diffusion ✓. Aquatic insects sometimes have tracheal gills ✓ to obtain oxygen from the water. Some pond snails use the inner surface of their mantle cavity as a lung ✓, occasionally replenishing their air supplies at the surface of the water.

🖉 This answer is worth 5 out of 10 marks. It is concise, but too brief. Furthermore, it concentrates entirely on *structural* adaptations. *Physiological* adaptations that could have been described would be the possession of a **circulatory system** and the use of **respiratory pigments**, together with explanations and appropriate examples.

Overall, Candidate A scores 37 out of 70 for this paper, which would be a grade D.

ock paper

Answers to mock paper 2: Candidate B

(1)

Feature	Wind-pollinated	Insect-pollinated
Large and colourful petals	✗	✔
Nectar present	✗	✔
Stamens usually hang outside the flower	✔	✗
Stigmas usually sticky and inside the flower	✔ ✗	✗ ✗

This answer receives 3 out of 4 marks. In wind-pollinated plants the stigmas are usually feathery and are found sticking out of the flower (in order to catch pollen in the air). The stigmas are usually sticky and inside the flower in insect-pollinated plants (in order that pollen from insects will become attached when the insects enter the flower in search of nectar).

(2) (a) A = epidermis ✓
B = cortex ✓

(b)

Pathway	Description
Apoplast ✗	The route by which water travels through the cytoplasm and plasmodesmata of plant cells.
Vacuolar ✓	The route by which water travels through the vacuoles of plant cells.
Symplast ✗	The route by which water travels through the cell walls of a plant.

This response receives 1 out of 3 marks. It is a fairly common mistake to mix up the apoplast and symplast pathways. Try to remember that the s**Y**mplast pathway involves water travelling through the c**Y**toplasm. Overall, Candidate B scores 3 out of 5 marks for this question.

(3) (a) (i) A = lacteal ✓
B = muscle ✓
(ii) 1 mm ✓

(b) It has a large surface area due to microvilli on the epithelial cells ✓ and it has a very good blood supply to carry away the absorbed products of digestion ✓.

A very clear answer to part (b) gives Candidate B 5 marks out of 5 for the whole question.

(4) (a) (i) A = sporophyte ✓
B = gametophyte ✓

(ii)

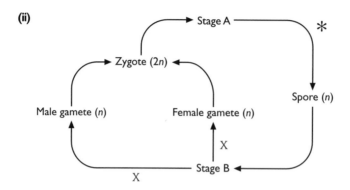

This is incorrect. Many students associate meiosis with gamete formation and therefore think that meiosis occurs in the gametophyte. However, note that the gametophyte is haploid (*n*) and so meiosis must have already occurred during spore production by the sporophyte (indicated by an asterisk on the diagram).

(b) During meiosis the homologous chromosomes exchange genetic material by crossing over at chiasmata ✓. The chromosomes also show independent assortment ✓. This means that gametes are genetically different from each other ✓ and so there will be genetic variation in the next generation.

A very good answer to part (b) gives the student 5 out of 6 marks for this question.

(5) (a) The loss of water vapour from a plant ✓ from stomata on leaves ✓.
(b) The lower epidermis ✓
(c) (i) The concentration of potassium ions falls by 69 arbitrary units in cell A ✓ but rises by 50 units and 186 units in cells B and C respectively ✓.
(ii) Stomata are kept open by the active transport of hydrogen ions out of the guard cells. When this process stops, hydrogen ions diffuse into the guard cells, causing potassium ions to diffuse out ✓. This causes the water potential in the guard cells to increase (become less negative) ✓ and so water moves out of the guard cells by osmosis ✓ (MAX). The guard cells become flaccid and the stoma closes.

An excellent answer to part (c) gives Candidate B full marks for this question.

(6) (a) (i) P = atria contracting ✓
(ii) QRS = ventricles contracting ✓
(iii) T = atria and ventricles relaxing ✓
(b) (i) Y ✓
(ii) Z ✓

A correct answer. The pressure will be highest just after leaving the heart (Y) and the oxygen concentration will be highest just after leaving the gills (Z).

(c) In fish the blood goes once around the body before being pumped again, but in mammals it goes twice around the body before being pumped again ✗.

🗩 This is incorrect (and certainly not enough for 3 marks!). In fact it is almost the opposite of what really happens. In a single circulation system, **the blood passes through the heart only once as it travels around the body**. This is not very efficient as a great deal of pressure is lost passing through the gas-exchange surface (gills), so the blood moves very slowly around the rest of the body. In a double circulation system, **the blood passes through the heart twice as it travels around the body**. This is **more efficient as the pressure is increased after the gas-exchange surface (lungs) by returning to the heart to be pumped to the rest of the body**. Candidate B scores 5 out of 8 marks for this question.

(7) (a) Diffusion ✓; active transport ✓; facilitated diffusion ✓

(b) $440 - 220 = 220$ ✓

$220/2$ ✓ $= 110 \, \mu g \, g^{-1} \, hour^{-1}$ ✓

(c) The fastest uptake at both temperatures occurs in the first 30 minutes ✓. The rate of uptake at 25°C is greater than at 10°C ✓.

🗩 This is correct and it is good to see the student using a *similarity* in a comparison question, as well as a difference. However, only two points have been made for a 3 mark question. The third mark would be available for a *comparison of figures from the graph*, such as **the final mass taken up at 25°C is 3 times greater than at 10°C**, or for stating that **the graph levels off at 10°C but keeps rising at 25°C**.

(d) An increase in temperature causes an increase in kinetic energy ✓ so diffusion is faster at 25°C ✓; active transport is also faster at 25°C ✓.

🗩 A good answer to part (d) earns Candidate B 11 out of 12 marks for this question.

(8) (a) (i) Between 12% and 14% oxygen, the volume of air inhaled decreases as oxygen concentration increases ✓. Above 14% oxygen, there is no change in the volume of air inhaled ✓.

(ii) Between 0% and 2% carbon dioxide, there is no change in the volume of air inhaled ✓; above 2% carbon dioxide, the volume of air inhaled increases as carbon dioxide concentration increases ✓.

(iii) 37% ✗

🗩 This is incorrect. More importantly, the student did not show any working, which could have earned up to 2 out of 3 marks. The correct answer is that at **3% carbon dioxide, the volume of air breathed per minute is 14 litres, and at 8% carbon dioxide, the volume of air breathed per minute is 68 litres; therefore the percentage increase is $[(68 - 14)/14] \times 100 = 385.7\%$**.

(b) The increase in carbon dioxide in the blood is detected by chemoreceptors ✓ in the aorta, carotid artery and medulla oblongata in the brain ✓ which sends signals to the lungs to increase the ventilation rate ✓.

(c) There is the same volume of nitrogen ✓ but the percentage is less because there is much more water vapour in expired air ✓.

🗩 Overall, Candidate B earns 9 out of 12 marks for this question.

(9) Small aquatic invertebrates, such as *Amoeba*, have a large surface area-to-volume ratio ✓ enabling them to take up the oxygen required by diffusion ✓. Bigger invertebrates, like flatworms, have flattened bodies to increase the surface area-to-volume ratio and decrease diffusion distances ✓. Aquatic insects may have tracheal gills ✓ or breathing tubes ✓ to obtain oxygen from the water or air respectively. Some pond snails use the inner surface of their mantle cavity as a lung ✓, periodically replenishing their air supplies at the surface. Leeches have a circulatory system to transport respiratory gases around the body ✓ and the blood contains haemoglobin (a respiratory pigment) to make oxygen carriage more efficient ✓. Water fleas also make haemoglobin, but only in the winter when the oxygen content of the water is lower (giving them a pink colour) ✓. Blood worms have gills ✓ as well as respiratory pigments, because they live in areas where oxygen concentration is low.

This is an excellent answer. It is concise and full of relevant detail, earning full marks.

Overall, Candidate B scores 59 out of 70 marks on this mock paper, which would be a grade A.

mock paper

Energy and the environment (I)

(1) The diagram below summarises the stages involved in the nitrogen cycle.

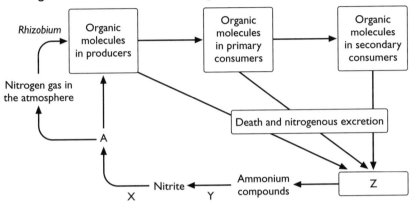

(a) (i) Name the type of compound labelled **A** in the diagram. (1 mark)

(ii) Name the types of bacteria labelled **X** and **Y** in the diagram. (2 marks)

(iii) What is the general name given to the group of organisms labelled **Z** in the diagram? (1 mark)

(b) 'Rhizobium lives in a mutualistic relationship with leguminous plants'. Explain what is meant by this statement. (3 marks)

The diagram below represents the cycling of nitrogen on a dairy farm. The width of the arrows represents the relative amount of nitrogen.

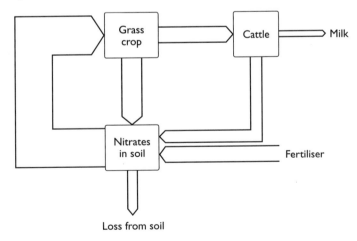

(c) Use information from the diagram to explain why it is necessary for a farmer to add fertiliser in order to maintain the production of milk. (3 marks)

Total: 10 marks

(2) The diagram below shows a simple food chain.

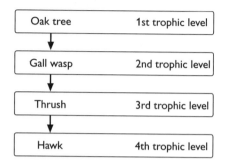

Oak tree	1st trophic level
Gall wasp	2nd trophic level
Thrush	3rd trophic level
Hawk	4th trophic level

(a) Explain what is meant by the term *trophic level*. (2 marks)

(b) Which of the organisms shown is:

    (i) a primary consumer

    (ii) a producer (2 marks)

(c) (i) What is shown by a pyramid of numbers? (2 marks)

    (ii) Sketch a pyramid of numbers that represents this food chain. (3 marks)

    (iii) State *one* way in which a pyramid of energy would differ from the pyramid of numbers for this food chain. (1 mark)

(d) Why is it rare to have more than four trophic levels in a single food chain? (2 marks)

Total: 12 marks

(3) The concentration of oxygen and the biomass of algae in a lake can vary with changes in the nutrient content of the water. The graph below shows the effect of the addition of phosphates on the oxygen concentration and the algal biomass in a freshwater lake. Observations were made as soon as the phosphates were added and for the next 8 weeks.

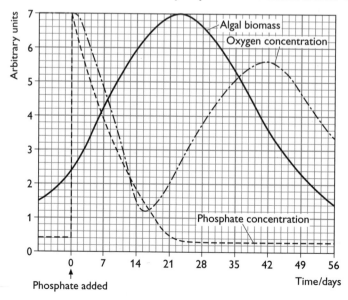

(a) State two possible sources of the phosphate. (2 marks)

(b) Describe how the algal biomass could have been estimated. (2 marks)

(c) Explain the relationship between the changes in the phosphate concentration and the algal biomass over the 8 week period. (3 marks)

(d) (i) Calculate the percentage decrease in oxygen concentration between days 7 and 14. Show your working. (3 marks)

(ii) Explain the changes in the oxygen concentration over the 8 week period. (4 marks)

(e) Suggest what effects the changes in the phosphate concentration might have on the number of different species present in the lake. (2 marks)

Total: 16 marks

Energy and the environment (II)

(1) The flow chart below summarises the decrease in biodiversity resulting from the pollution of a lake.

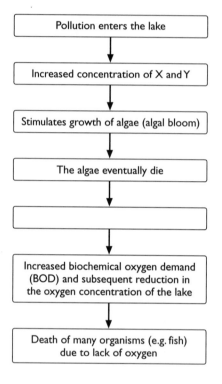

| Pollution enters the lake |
| Increased concentration of X and Y |
| Stimulates growth of algae (algal bloom) |
| The algae eventually die |
| |
| Increased biochemical oxygen demand (BOD) and subsequent reduction in the oxygen concentration of the lake |
| Death of many organisms (e.g. fish) due to lack of oxygen |

(a) (i) What is the name given to the process shown in the flow chart? (1 mark)

(ii) State two possible sources of pollution in this case. (2 marks)

(iii) Identify the chemical compounds labelled **X** and **Y** in the flow chart. (2 marks)

(iv) Complete the flow chart by inserting the missing step into the empty box provided. (2 marks)

The oxygen concentration of a sample of polluted water was measured over a period of 15 minutes. The results are shown in the table below.

Time/minutes	Oxygen concentration/mg dm^{-3}
0	13.4
5	10.8
10	8.7
15	6.6

(b) Calculate the biochemical oxygen demand (BOD) of this polluted water. Show your working.

(3 marks)

Total: 10 marks

(2) The diagram below shows the flow of energy through a food chain. (All units are in kilojoules per square metre per year.)

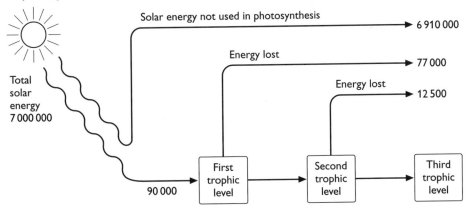

Solar energy not used in photosynthesis → 6 910 000

Energy lost → 77 000

Energy lost → 12 500

Total solar energy 7 000 000

90 000 → First trophic level → Second trophic level → Third trophic level

(a) Suggest two reasons why not all of the solar energy can be used in photosynthesis.

(2 marks)

(b) Explain what is meant by the following terms:
  (i) gross primary production
  (ii) net primary production

(4 marks)

(c) Using the values shown on the diagram, calculate the percentage of the gross primary production that becomes available as net primary production. Show your working.

(2 marks)

(d) Suggest why the overall energy loss from the first trophic level is greater than that from the second trophic level.

(3 marks)

(e) Suggest why there are generally more trophic levels in an aquatic food chain than in a terrestrial food chain.

(3 marks)

Total: 14 marks

(3) The diagram below summarises the carbon cycle.

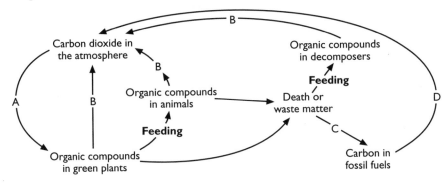

B

Carbon dioxide in the atmosphere

Organic compounds in decomposers

B

Feeding

A   B   Organic compounds in animals   Death or waste matter   D

Feeding

C

Organic compounds in green plants

Carbon in fossil fuels

(a) Complete the table below to show whether combustion, respiration, photosynthesis or fossilisation are represented by letters **A** to **D**.

Process	Letter
Combustion	
Respiration	
Photosynthesis	
Fossilisation	

(4 marks)

The graph below shows the world use of coal between 1950 and 1990.

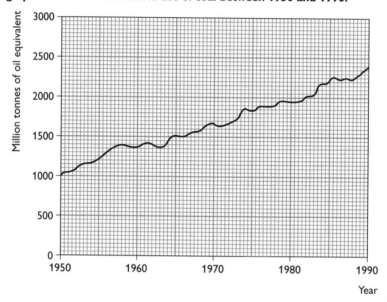

(b) (i) Calculate the percentage increase in coal use during this period.
Show your working. (3 marks)

(ii) Suggest *two* advantages of coal as a form of fuel. (2 marks)

The chief disadvantage of burning fossil fuels lies in their impact on the environment, due to the release of polluting gases. This might lead to the *greenhouse effect*.

(c) (i) Name *two* gases that contribute to the greenhouse effect. (2 marks)

(ii) Explain how the greenhouse effect might lead to global warming. (2 marks)

(iii) Suggest *one* environmental consequence of global warming. (1 mark)

Total: 14 marks

Answers to mock paper 3: Candidate A

(1) (a) (i) A = amino acid ✗

> 🖋 Amino acids are made by producers. A is **nitrate**.

(ii) X = Nitrosomonas ✗; Y = Nitrobacter ✗

> 🖋 This is a fairly common error, mixing up the two types of bacteria. Remember that Nitroso**MON**as acts on am**MON**ium compounds.

(iii) Decomposers ✓

(b) They both gain from the relationship. ✓

> 🖋 This is correct, but not detailed enough for more than 1 mark. Candidate A should have stated *how* they both gain from the relationship. The plant gains a source of organic nitrogen which has been fixed by *Rhizobium* and the bacteria (living in nodules on the plant roots) gain carbohydrate from the plant.

(c) Nitrates are lost from the soil ✓ and taken out of the cycle in milk ✓. Therefore, fertiliser must be added to replace the nitrogen or the nitrate supply will decline, causing a reduction in the grass crop and hence in milk production ✓.

> 🖋 A good answer to part (c), worth full marks. Overall, Candidate A scores 5 out of 10 marks for this question.

(2) (a) The position occupied by an organism in a food chain ✓.

> 🖋 This is correct, but only worth 1 mark. Candidate A should have expanded this definition, perhaps by giving an example — the first trophic level is always occupied by a producer, such as a green plant.

(b) (i) Hawk ✗

> 🖋 The hawk is a *tertiary* consumer. The primary consumer is the **gall wasp**.

(ii) Oak tree ✓

(c) (i) The number of organisms at each trophic level in a food chain ✓ at a particular time ✓.

(ii)

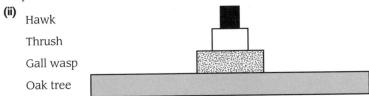

Hawk

Thrush

Gall wasp

Oak tree

e This is worth 2 out of 3 marks. It is the right way up, symmetrical and correctly labelled. However, the size of the 'blocks' is incorrect. These should be in proportion to the number of organisms at each trophic level, so the block for oak trees should be *smaller* than that for gall wasps (there are fewer trees than there are wasps).

(iii) The blocks would be different sizes ✗.

e This is a very vague answer and not worth a mark. The distinctive feature of a pyramid of energy is that it is always 'upright', i.e. the largest block is at the bottom (producers). This is not the case for the pyramid of numbers in this question.

(d) Energy is lost between trophic levels ✓.

e This is correct, but it does not go far enough for the second mark. Because energy is lost between each trophic level, it is rare for there to be sufficient energy left in the system to sustain a fifth level. Overall, Candidate A scores 7 out of 12 marks for this question.

(3) (a) Detergents ✓; fertilisers ✓

e Another possible answer to part (a) would be **untreated sewage**.

(b) By finding the total mass of living algae ✓.

e This is not enough for 2 marks. Algal biomass is the total mass of living algae in a given area **at a particular time**.

(c) As phosphate concentration increases, so does algal biomass ✓.

e This is correct. The addition of phosphate *does* stimulate algal growth, i.e. an increase in biomass, but Candidate A has not described what happens as the phosphate concentration *falls*. **Phosphate is used up** by the increased numbers of algae, **so the algal biomass falls**, due to a lack of this nutrient.

(d) (i) Oxygen concentration falls from 5 to $1\frac{1}{2}$ units ✓ so the percentage decrease is $(3\frac{1}{2}/100) \times 5 = 0.175\%$ ✗.

e This answer earns 1 out of 3 marks. The figures are taken correctly from the graph and Candidate B uses the difference $(3\frac{1}{2})$ for the calculation. However, the candidate gets confused about how to calculate a percentage change. Remember that the formula is **(change/original value) × 100**. The correct answer is therefore **$(3\frac{1}{2} \div 5) \times 100 = 70\%$.**

(ii) The oxygen concentration falls in the first 2 weeks as it is being used by aerobic bacteria in the sewage ✓. It then gradually returns to normal during weeks 2 to 6, due to the death of the sewage bacteria ✓.

e This response is worth 2 out of 4 marks. Oxygen concentration can also increase between weeks 2 to 6 due to **photosynthesis by the algae**. The student has also not explained the fall in oxygen concentration from weeks 6 to 8. This is due to the

death of the algae and their consequent **decomposition by aerobic bacteria,** increasing the **biochemical oxygen demand**.

(e) It will not change ✗.

🖉 This answer is not worth a mark. It is likely that the number of species will decrease initially, due to the high phosphate concentrations and blocking of light by the algal bloom. Towards the end of the study, we might expect the number of species to recover a little, as the phosphate concentration decreases and the algae die. Candidate A scores 7 out of 16 marks for this question.

Overall, Candidate A scores 19 out of 38 marks for this mock paper, which is a grade D/E.

Answers to mock paper 3: Candidate B

(1) (a) (i) B = nitrate ✓

(ii) X = Nitrobacter ✓; Y = Nitrosomonas ✓

(iii) Decomposers ✓

(b) Mutualism refers to a relationship between two different species which results in benefit to both ✓. In this case, the plant gains a source of organic nitrogen which has been fixed by *Rhizobium* ✓ and the bacteria (living in nodules on the plant roots) gain carbohydrate from the plant ✓.

(c) Nitrates are lost from the soil ✓. Fertiliser must be added to replace this nitrogen or the nitrate supply will decline, causing a reduction in the grass crop and a subsequent drop in milk production ✓.

The answer to part (c) is worth 2 out of 3 marks. Candidate B should also have mentioned that **nitrogen is taken out of the cycle in milk**. Overall, this answer scores 9 out of 10 marks.

(2) (a) The position occupied by an organism in a food chain ✓. For example, the first trophic level is always occupied by a producer, such as a green plant ✓.

(b) (i) Gall wasp ✓

(ii) Oak tree ✓

(c) (i) The number of organisms at each trophic level in a food chain ✓

This is worth only 1 mark. The second mark would be awarded for stating that it is the number of organisms **present at a particular time**.

(ii)

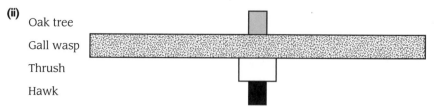

Oak tree

Gall wasp

Thrush

Hawk

This is worth 2 out of 3 marks. The numbers look reasonable and the pyramid is symmetrical. It is, however, upside down. Remember that the producer always goes at the bottom of a pyramid.

(iii) A producer (oak tree) would have the largest area on the pyramid ✓.

(d) Energy is lost between trophic levels ✓ so it is rare that there is sufficient energy left in the system to sustain a fifth level ✓.

Overall, Candidate B scores 10 out of 12 marks for this question.

(3) (a) Untreated sewage ✓; fertilisers ✓

🖉 Another possible answer to part (a) would be **detergents**.

(b) By finding the total mass of living algae ✓ in a given area at a particular time ✓.

(c) Algal growth was originally limited by the lack of phosphate ✓. Therefore, addition of phosphate stimulated algal growth, i.e. an increase in biomass ✓. Phosphate was used up by increased numbers of algae ✓ (MAX), so algal biomass fell, due to lack of phosphate.

(d) (i) Oxygen concentration fell from 5 to $1\frac{1}{2}$ units ✓, so the percentage decrease was $(1\frac{1}{2} \div 5)$ ✗ $\times 100 = 30\%$ ✓

🖉 This answer earns 2 out of 3 marks. The figures are taken correctly from the graph, but Candidate B does not use the **difference** $(3\frac{1}{2})$ for the calculation. However, he or she does remember to divide by 5 and multiply by 100 and so has only really made one mistake. The correct answer is $(3\frac{1}{2} \div 5) \times 100 = 70\%$.

(ii) The oxygen concentration fell in the first 2 weeks as it was being used by aerobic bacteria in the sewage ✓. It then gradually returned to normal during weeks 2 to 6, due to the death of the sewage bacteria ✓ and photosynthesis by the algae ✓. The oxygen concentration then fell again between weeks 6 to 8, due to the death of the algae and their consequent decomposition by aerobic bacteria (increasing biochemical oxygen demand) ✓.

🖉 This is an excellent answer, earning full marks.

(e) It will decrease ✓.

🖉 This answer is *just* worth a mark. It is likely that the number of species will decrease initially, due to some of them being unable to survive in high phosphate concentrations. Furthermore, the algal bloom may block out light to other plants so these plants (and any other species dependent upon them) might die. Towards the end of the study, we might expect the number of species to recover a little, as the phosphate concentration decreases and the algae die. The student scores 14 out of 16 marks for this question.

Overall, Candidate B scores 33 out of 38 marks for this paper, which would be a grade A.

Answers to mock paper 4: Candidate A

(1) (a) (i) Pollution ✗

📝 This process is known as **eutrophication**.

(ii) Fertiliser ✓; sewage ✓

(iii) X = nitrate ✓; Y = phosphate ✓

(iv) Increase in respiration ✓ of aerobic decomposers ✓

(b) Oxygen concentration falls from 13.4 to 6.6 mg dm^{-3} ✓. Therefore the BOD is (13.4 − 6.6) = 6.8 mg.

📝 This answer is worth 1 out of 3 marks. BOD is the quantity of oxygen removed by microorganisms from a sample of water in a given time. Therefore, the calculation is incorrect (or at least incomplete) and the units are not correct. In this case BOD = (6.8/15) × 60 = 27.2 mg O$_2$ dm^{-3} hour^{-1} *or* 6.8/15 = 0.453 mg O$_2$ dm^{-3} min^{-1}. Overall, Candidate A scores 7 out of 10 marks for this question.

(2) (a) It might be reflected off clouds ✓. If it meets a plant, it might land on an area which does not photosynthesise ✓.

(b) (i) The net primary production that is actually available to primary consumers, i.e. net primary production less the energy used in respiration by the plant ✗.

(ii) The synthesis of biomass in producers, by photosynthesis ✗.

📝 Candidate A has confused these two terms, getting them the wrong way around. Remember that gross production is always greater than net production.

(c) (90 000 / 13 000) × 100 = 692.3% ✗

📝 This would be worth 1 mark for realising that you must multiply by 100 to get a percentage. However, the answer is clearly not correct. You cannot have *more* energy available as net primary production than as gross primary production. The student has got the figures upside-down. The correct answer is **(13 000/90 000) × 100 = 14.4%**.

(d) Not all of the producer is eaten ✓.

📝 This is correct, but only worth 1 out of 3 marks. Remember that you must make three separate points for 3 marks. Candidate A could have said that some parts of the producer might be underground, or that some of the eaten material might not be digested, i.e. end up as faeces.

(e) The productivity of aquatic producers is higher than that of terrestrial producers ✓ so there is more net primary production available to consumers ✓. Energy transfer is also more efficient in an aquatic system ✓.

e This is a very good answer, worth full marks. Overall, Candidate A scores 7 out of 14 for this question.

(3) (a)

Process	Letter
Combustion	D ✓
Respiration	A ✗
Photosynthesis	B ✗
Fossilisation	C ✓

e This answer is worth 2 out of 4 marks. Candidate A has confused the processes of respiration and photosynthesis. Note that A *must* be photosynthesis as it is the only process that fixes carbon dioxide into living matter (green plants).

(b) (i) Coal use rises from 1000 to 2400 ✓ so the percentage increase is:
$(100/1400) \times 1000 = 71.4\%$ ✗

e This answer earns 1 out of 3 marks. The figures are taken correctly from the graph and Candidate A uses the difference (1400) for the calculation. However, the candidate has forgotten how to calculate a percentage change. Remember that the formula is **(change/original value) × 100**. The correct answer is therefore $(1400/1000) \times 100 = 140\%$.

(ii) Cheap ✓; does not cause much pollution ✗

e Coal *is* relatively cheap, but it *does* cause pollution (as indicated in the rest of the question).

(c) (i) Carbon dioxide ✓; methane ✓
(ii) The gases prevent some of the heat from the sun leaving the atmosphere ✓.

e This is correct, but only worth 1 mark. We need some of the gases in the atmosphere to keep the temperature high enough to sustain life. However, as the concentration of gases increases, more heat is trapped and the temperature rises. It is this effect that causes global warming.

(iii) Melting of polar icecaps, leading to flooding ✓

e Overall, Candidate A earns 8 out of 14 marks for this question.

Candidate A manages a total score for this mock paper of 22 out of 38 marks, which would be a grade D.

Answers to mock paper 4: Candidate B

(1) (a) (i) Eutrophication ✓
    (ii) Fertiliser ✓; sewage ✓
    (iii) X = nitrate ✓; Y = phosphate ✓
    (iv) Increase in decomposers ✓

> The answer to part (iv) is only worth 1 mark of the available 2. A better answer is an **increase in the respiration of aerobic decomposers**. This makes it clear that it is aerobic respiration that causes the increase in BOD in the next part of the flow chart.

(b) Oxygen concentration falls from 13.4 to 6.6 mg dm^{-3} ✓, therefore the BOD is $(13.4 - 6.6) = 6.8/15 \times 60 = 27.2\ \text{mg O}_2\,\text{dm}^{-3}\text{hour}^{-1}$ ✓✓.

> Overall, Candidate B scores **9 out of 10 marks** for this question.

(2) (a) It might not reach the plants ✓. If it meets a plant, it might be reflected rather than absorbed ✓.
(b) (i) The synthesis of biomass by producers ✓ by photosynthesis ✓
    (ii) The gross primary production that is actually available to primary consumers ✓

> This is correct, but it does not explain why gross and net primary production are different. Net primary production is equal to gross primary production *less* the energy used in respiration by the plant.

(c) $(13\,000/90\,000) \times 100$ ✓ $= 14.4\%$ ✓
(d) Not all of the producer is eaten ✓. For example some parts may be underground ✓. Some of the eaten material might not be digested and end up as faeces ✓.
(e) Productivity in aquatic producers is higher than in terrestrial producers ✓ so more net primary production is available to consumers ✓.

> This is worth 2 out of 3 marks. The student could also have mentioned that **energy transfer between trophic levels is more efficient in an aquatic system**, or that there are **lower respiratory losses in aquatic systems**. Overall, Candidate B scores **12 out of 14** for this question.

(3) (a)

Process	Letter
Combustion	D ✓
Respiration	B ✓
Photosynthesis	A ✓
Fossilisation	C ✓

(b) (i) Coal use rises from 1000 to 2400 ✓ so the percentage increase is: (1400/1000) × 100 ✓ = 140% ✓

(ii) Cheap ✓; easy to extract and store ✓

(c) (i) Carbon dioxide ✓; chlorofluorocarbons (CFCs) ✗

🖉 CFCs are *not* greenhouse gases. Either **methane** or **oxides of nitrogen** would be worth the second mark.

(ii) The gases prevent some of the heat from the sun leaving the atmosphere ✓. As the concentration of gases increases, more heat is trapped and the temperature rises ✓.

(iii) Melting of polar icecaps, leading to flooding ✓

🖉 Overall, the student earns 13 out of 14 marks for this question.

Candidate B achieves a total score for this mock paper of 34 out of 38 marks, which would be a grade A.